Solid·State
Magnetism

John Crangle

Professor of Physics, University of Sheffield

Edward Arnold

A division of Hodder & Stoughton

LONDON   MELBOURNE   AUCKLAND

© 1991 John Crangle

First published in Great Britain 1991

British Library Cataloguing in Publication Data
Crangle, John
  Solid state magnetism.
  I. Title
  538

  ISBN 0–340–54552–6

Typeset in 10 on 11 pt Times by Wearside Tradespools, Fulwell,
Sunderland.
Printed in Great Britain for Edward Arnold, a division of Hodder
and Stoughton Limited, Mill Road, Dunton Green, Sevenoaks, Kent
TW13 2YA by St Edmundsbury Press Ltd, Bury St Edmunds,
Suffolk and bound by Hartnolls Ltd, Bodmin, Cornwall.

Preface

Solid state magnetism is important and attempts to understand magnetic properties have led to an increasingly deep insight into the fundamental make up of solids. Both experimental and theoretical research into magnetism continue to be very active, yet there is still much ground to cover before there can be a full understanding.

There is a strong interplay between the developments of materials science and of magnetism. Hundreds of new materials have been discovered, often with previously unobserved and puzzling magnetic properties. A large and growing technology exists that is based on the magnetic properties of materials. Very many devices used in everyday life involve magnetism and new applications are being invented all the time. Understanding the fundamental background to the applications is vital to using and developing them.

The aim of this book is to provide a simple, up-to-date introduction to the study of solid state magnetism, both intrinsic and technical. It is designed to meet the needs and interests of advanced undergraduate students reading physics; of postgraduates in physical and materials sciences and in engineering; and also those of the practising scientist specializing in another area who requires an introduction to magnetism. The focus is to explain the bulk magnetic properties of solid materials in atomic terms and to introduce some of their applications. The subject matter is treated selectively rather than comprehensively. The size of the book is limited so that those who are studying several other topics simultaneously may grasp most of the contents fairly readily. Also, being small enough and perhaps sufficiently cheap, it is hoped that the book will be accessible to students for them to own themselves. This book is essentially a development of another book entitled 'The magnetic properties of solids' which was published in 1977.

Early chapters cover the fundamentals of the atomic nature of magnetism. There is then a full section on the techniques of a wide range of magnetic measurements including the use of quantum interference in magnetism. Chapter five is on the interplay between neutron scattering and magnetism. It deals with elastic and inelastic scattering and how these relate to magnetic excitations and spin waves. Modern developments using polarized neutrons and their uses are covered. Then there is a chapter dealing with antiferromagnetism, ferrimagnetism and non-collinear magnetic order which includes spin glasses, magnetic amorphous alloys and the relevance to high-T_C superconducting ceramics. Other fundamental topics are mechanisms of exchange interaction, hyperfine fields and domain magnetism. The final chapter covers a selection of applications of magnetism. Many important topics are omitted for the reason that they are not yet seen as essential to a general understanding and that the reader can move on to study these with the material of this book as background. Examples are the magnetism of solid surfaces, magnetic multilayers and heavy fermion materials.

The system of units used is SI and a conversion chart between SI and cgs is given in Chapter one. No choice is made between the Sommerfeld and the Kennelly systems of magnetic units but a distinctive nomenclature is employed which should enable either to be used where appropriate, avoiding ambiguity. Susceptibilities are defined so that conversion between SI and cgs only requires movement of the decimal point.

The author is grateful to all those friends, collaborators and teachers who have influenced the development of his interest in magnetism, and also to many of his own students who by their questioning have taught him much more than they are aware.

All the diagrams except two were drawn by the author using a microcomputer and direct Postscript coding that was developed on a very good word processor. John Hunt and Judy McEwan provided excellent support for this. The author expresses his warmest gratitude to his colleague Mrs Yvonne Platt for all her generous industry, skill and patience, especially in converting an almost illegible scribble into an extremely clear typescript. Permission from the respective copyright holders to reproduce Figures 8.18 and 9.5 is hereby acknowledged.

The author is greatly indebted to his wife and family for all their support and encouragement, and for putting up with it all.

John Crangle
1991

Contents

Index of Symbols

I	Nuclear spin	7.2
I	Magnetization per unit volume (cgs)	1.2
J,L,S,M_J,n,l,s,m_l,m_s		
	Atomic and electronic quantum numbers	2.2
J	Magnetic polarization	1.2
J,L,S	Angular momentum vectors	2.2
$K_1, K_2 \ldots$	Empirical anisotropy constants	8.1.1
k	Boltzmann constant $= 1{\cdot}3807 \times 10^{-23}\,\mathrm{J\,K^{-1}}$	2.2.3
M	Magnetization per unit volume	1.2
m_k	Kennelly polarization dipole moment	1.2
m^*	Effective electron mass	3.2.1
m	Electronic mass $= 9{\cdot}1095 \times 10^{-31}\,\mathrm{kg}$	2.1
m_s	Sommerfeld magnetization dipole moment	1.2
N_s	Number of atoms per unit mass	2.6
N	Avogadro number $= 6{\cdot}022 \times 10^{23}\,\mathrm{mole^{-1}}$	2.6
P	Cooper pair total momentum	4.3.1
p_{eff}	Effective paramagnetic Bohr magneton number	2.4
p	Ferromagnetic magneton number	3.5.2
Q	Quality factor for magnetic bubble materials	9.4
q	Molecular field coefficient	6.1.1
q	Crystal momentum	5.4
R	Gas constant	1.1.1
r	Radius of electron orbit	2.1
S_m	Magnetic entropy	1.1.1
S	Spin quantum number	1.1.1
T_N	Néel temperature	1.1.4
T_C	Curie temperature	1.1.1
T_f	Spin glass freezing temperature	6.5
U	Magnetic scalar potential	4.6.9
V	Volume of specimen	1.2
v	Velocity	2.1
W_J	Spin-orbit coupling energy	2.2.2
$\alpha_1,\alpha_2,\alpha_3$	Direction cosines	8.1.3
α_J	Van Vleck contribution to paramagnetic susceptibility	2.4
θ'	Molecular field parameter with dimensions of temperature	3.1
θ_p	Paramagnetic Curie temperature	1.1.2
θ	Diffraction Bragg angle	5.3.4
γ_m	Molecular field coefficient	2.6
γ	Magnetomechanical ratio	2.1
δ	Domain wall thickness	8.1.3
δ_1	Domain wall thickness parameter	8.1.3

Chapter 1 _____

Introduction

The magnetic properties of solids are important and attempts to understand them have led to a deep insight into the fundamental structure of many solids, both metallic and non-metallic. The understanding is still far from complete. As new phenomena have been discovered and more theory has been developed, new and deeper questions have emerged. As in other areas of science the need to test theories that have themselves been set up to explain and correlate previous experimental information suggests new experimental approaches. These have led to further theoretical development, and so on. This process has been accelerated in recent years by the development of new experimental techniques. A very wide variety of magnetic behaviour has now been recognized in hundreds of different materials. One of the problems in magnetism is that there are serious mathematical difficulties in tackling parts of the subject with theories that are very realistic. Furthermore, it has not yet been possible in many areas to devise sufficiently sensitive experiments to test theoretical predictions and so to give an indication of which among diverging branches in a theory is correct. However, theory based on one-dimensional or two-dimensional simplifications can now be tested as a result of the discovery of materials with quasi-one and quasi-two dimensional magnetic properties. The range of available magnetic materials produced both by metallurgy and by chemistry is so very large that many examples have been found experimentally which satisfy the conditions of the simplified theory, often verifying it in a remarkable way.

In addition to the fundamental interest in the magnetic properties of solids there are very many important applications of magnetic materials. Magnetism is often divided into two kinds. The first is called intrinsic magnetism, concerned with relating magnetic properties to electronic structure and other fundamentals in metals or non-metals. The second, technical magnetism, is concerned largely with the properties of magnetic domains and related phenomena. There is naturally cross coupling between the two groups.

The aim of this book is to provide a simple introduction to magnetism in solids, both intrinsic and technical. The level of the treatment is intended to be that of a senior undergraduate studying physics in a British university, although hopefully it will meet the needs of a wider group than this. The treatment is experimental and descriptive, with an accent on the basic principles involved. The rest of this first chapter is devoted mainly to an outline of the more obvious experimental magnetic properties, to highlight the needs for the explanations which follow.

1.1 Basic magnetic properties

That lodestone (magnetite, Fe_3O_4), a natural non-metallic solid, may attract iron was first described in known Greek writings at about 800 BC. Its scientific significance was not appreciated until some time later. This was the first technical magnetic material because it formed the first compass.

1.1.1 Ferromagnetic materials

The widely recognized ferromagnetic elements are iron, nickel and cobalt. The most obvious properties of a ferromagnet are as follows.

If a piece of iron is examined at room temperature it may be obtained first in an unmagnetized state. If it is then placed in a relatively weak magnetic field a magnetic moment is induced. Such a field may be produced by wrapping a few turns of wire round the iron specimen and passing an electric current of the order of one ampere through it, or by placing the specimen in the vicinity of a permanent magnet. The magnetic state of the iron specimen depends on the magnetic field in a relatively complicated way. There are also differences in the definition of the magnetic state according to how it is measured.

The different measuring techniques are described in Chapter 4. The magnetization is given by a measurement depending on the dipole moment of the specimen. An example would be to measure the change in field at some point outside the specimen due to the presence of the specimen. Alternatively the induction within the specimen can be measured from the charge flowing in a closed electrical circuit when the specimen is inserted or removed from it. The difference is that the induction includes in it the contribution of induction which would be produced by the applied field itself if the specimen were absent. While the magnetization is used more in fundamental measurements of ferromagnetic properties, the induction is used technically. The relationship between the quantities differs according to the unit convention used and there is an unfortunate dichotomy between users. The unit systems are described in Section 1.2. The various quantities will now be used according to how they are defined there.

Starting with the unmagnetized piece of iron at room temperature we find that when a small increasing field is applied its magnetization increases at first slowly and reversibly. Beyond a critical field hysteresis develops. The magnetization does not return to zero when the field is switched off and if the field is cycled between small limits a minor hysteresis loop is followed. Eventually the magnetization rises more sharply with increasing field and at still higher fields saturation of the magnetization sets in. The

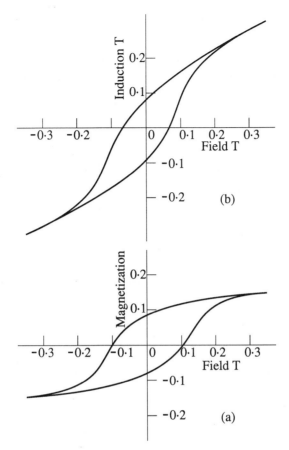

Figure 1.1 Magnetization (a) and induction (b) hysteresis loops of a hard magnetic material. In (a) the unit used for the y-axis is $\mu_0 M$, equal to the magnetic polarization J.

hysteresis loop from saturation is a characteristic of the specimen and it is illustrated in Figure 1.1a. The remanence is thereby defined, which is the magnetization remaining when the field is switched off from saturation; and the coercivity is also defined, which is the reverse field required to reduce the magnetization to zero from saturation. The induction hysteresis loop has a different shape (Fig. 1.1b) and the induction coercivity has a different value. The hysteresis properties of ferromagnets are largely properties of arrangements of magnetic domains and these are described in Chapter 8.

After saturation has been reached the magnetization increases very slowly and approximately linearly with increasing field. Under some conditions it is constant. This is the intrinsic magnetization, which is the value of the magnetization within a domain and is what remains when the different orientations of all the domains present have been allowed for. It is reached in strong fields because of the effect of increasing field on the domain orientation. The intrinsic magnetization of a ferromagnet does not become zero when the applied field is zero but it remains at a value equal to or only a little below its value in a strong field. This is the spontaneous magnetization, which is spontaneously present within the domains when no field is applied externally. In iron at room temperature the difference between the spontaneous magnetization and the intrinsic magnetization measured in a strong field of about 5 T (50 kOe) is only detectable with difficulty.

The spontaneous magnetization depends on temperature (Fig. 1.2), having its largest value at the absolute zero. It falls at an increasing rate with increasing temperature and becomes zero at a characteristic temperature T_C called the Curie temperature. As the temperature rises the intrinsic magnetization varies increasingly with field (Fig. 1.3) and it becomes non-linearly dependent on the field as the Curie temperature is approached. This causes certain difficulties in measuring the spontaneous magnetization when T approaches T_C, with consequent problems in the exact experimental definition of T_C from magnetization measurements. The maximum value of the spontaneous magnetization (at $T = 0$) is directly related to the average magnetic moment per atom of the ferromagnet and it gives a measure of the number of magnetic carriers per atom.

If the magnetization of a single crystal of a ferromagnet is measured for field increasing from zero it is found that the approach to saturation differs

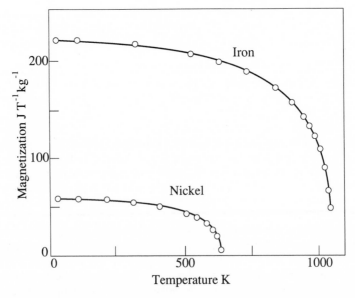

Figure 1.2 Spontaneous magnetization plotted against temperature for iron and nickel.

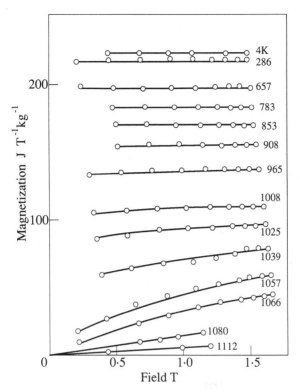

Figure 1.3 Magnetization of iron plotted against field for different temperatures (K).

according to the orientation of the field with respect to the crystal axes. Some directions are directions of easy magnetization and others are hard directions. In iron (Fig. 1.4) the cube edge direction (100) is easy while the direction of the cube diagonal (111) is hard. This is a fundamental effect called magnetocrystalline anisotropy. The directionality of the magnetic moments of individual atoms interacts with the symmetry of their crystalline environment. Measurements of the effect lead to basic information on the nature of the magnetic atoms: a very important effect in technical magnetism. Magnetocrystalline energy plays a large part in determining the thickness, energy and mobility of domain boundary walls; important in both soft and hard technical magnetic materials.

Another effect observed in ferromagnets is the occurrence of small dimensional changes. The state of strain alters as the direction of the spontaneous magnetization rotates with respect to the crystal axes. This is magnetostriction. There is also a small volume magnetostriction as the spontaneous magnetization is altered by changing the temperature. Magnetostriction is also fundamental and is due to the link between atomic magnetic moments and the crystalline lattice. It is important in technical

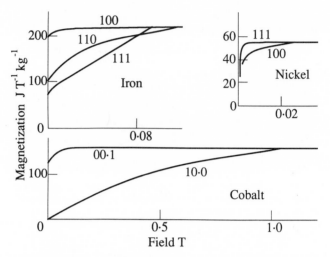

Figure 1.4 Magnetization of single crystals of iron, nickel and cobalt, plotted against field for different crystallographic directions.

magnetism, affecting the pinning of domain wall boundaries to crystalline imperfections.

The specific heat capacity of ferromagnetic materials contains a significant magnetic component C_m superimposed on that part of the total specific heat capacity (mostly from the lattice and from the conduction electron gas) which would be present if the material were non-magnetic. The sharp cusp in the graph of heat capacity against temperature (Fig. 1.5) at the Curie temperature is typical of a second order thermodynamic phase change. It is associated with the disappearance of long-range magnetic order at T_C. The small magnetic heat capacity remaining just above T_C arises from the presence of residual short-range magnetic order, the amount of which diminishes rapidly with increasing temperature. The entropy ΔS_m of the magnetic state may be obtained from measurement of the heat capacity.

It is given by

$$\Delta S_m = \int C_m / T \, dT$$

evaluated over the whole range of temperature of the ferromagnetic state. The entropy of the magnetic state is related to the spin quantum number S (and hence the magnetic moment) of the magnetic atoms by

$$\Delta S_m = cR \ln(2S + 1)$$

where c is the fraction of the atoms present carrying the magnetic moment and R is the gas constant.

There is also a link between the magnetic state of a ferromagnet and its electrical resistivity. The dependence of the resistivity is illustrated in Figure 1.6. A discussion of the relationship between magnetic order and

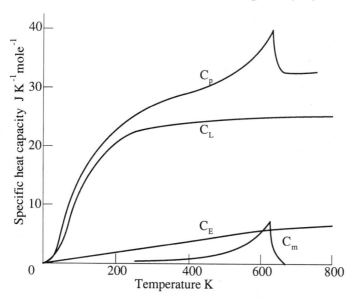

Figure 1.5 Specific heat capacity of nickel, as a function of temperature. The contributions to the total (C_p) are from the lattice (C_L), the electrons (C_E) and the magnetic (C_M) part.

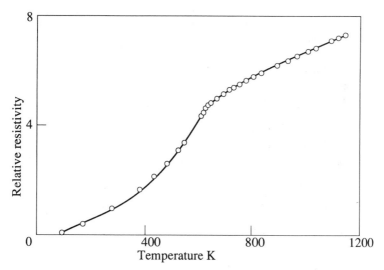

Figure 1.6 The resistivity of nickel (relative to its value at 273 K) as a function of temperature. The Curie temperature is 631 K.

resistivity is beyond the scope of this book. Since disorder of any kind contributes to resistivity we may expect the onset of magnetic order when a ferromagnetic specimen is cooled through its Curie temperature to be accompanied by a fall in resistivity.

1.1.2 Paramagnetism

Many solids are paramagnetic. When a field is applied to them they become magnetized, usually much more weakly than a ferromagnetic material. The magnetization depends linearly on the field and it always disappears when the field is removed (Fig. 1.7). The rate of change of magnetization with field is called the paramagnetic susceptibility, referred to unit mass of the specimen (χ), to one mole (χ_m) or to unit volume (κ).

Above their Curie temperature ferromagnetics become paramagnetic and their susceptibility depends on temperature. The reciprocal of the susceptibility varies linearly with temperature, or nearly so (Fig. 1.8), with an intercept on the positive temperature axis at the paramagnetic Curie temperature θ_p, which is usually close to T_C, though the two quantities are rarely exactly equal. This dependence of susceptibility on temperature of the form

$$\chi = C/(T - \theta_p)$$

is known as the Curie-Weiss law, where C is the Curie constant per unit mass.

Some other materials, of which ordinary hydrated copper sulphate $CuSO_4 . 5H_2O$ is an example (Fig. 1.9) follow a similar law at all ordinary temperatures but for them θ_p is zero. This becomes the Curie law, $\chi = C/T$. Negative values of θ_p are also found, often in antiferromagnetics above their Néel temperature. The constants C and θ_p are related to fundamental properties of the atoms or ions of the materials. They are discussed in Chapter 2.

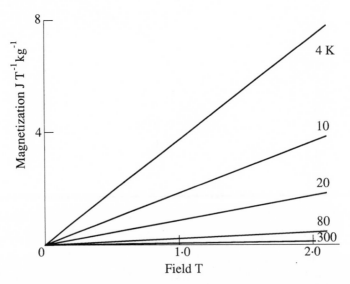

Figure 1.7 Magnetization of hydrated copper sulphate $CuSO_4 . 5H_2O$ as a function of field at different temperatures.

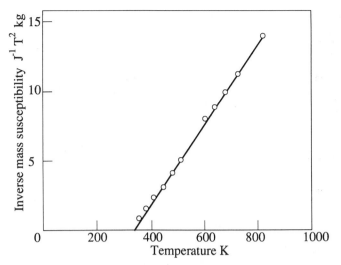

Figure 1.8 The reciprocal of the mass susceptibility of a 32 per cent nickel–copper alloy plotted against temperature. This illustrates the Curie-Weiss law. θ_p is 336 K.

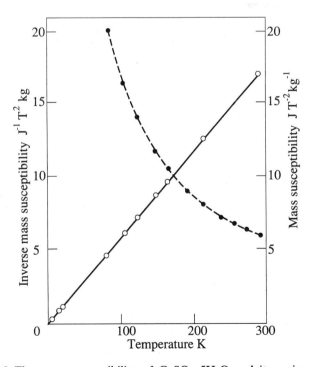

Figure 1.9 The mass susceptibility of $CuSO_4 \cdot 5H_2O$ and its reciprocal, plotted against temperature. This illustrates the Curie Law.

Many non-ferromagnetic metals are paramagnetic but their susceptibility is relatively weak and it depends little or not at all on temperature (Fig. 3.1). In such materials the paramagnetism is generally a property of electrons contained in relatively broad energy bands associated with the metallic state, and not so much related to electrons tightly bound into the ion cores of the atoms making up the metal. The properties of materials of this kind are discussed in Chapter 3.

1.1.3 Diamagnetism

Diamagnetic substances have a negative magnetic susceptibility. All substances have a basic diamagnetism that is nearly always weak and is very often masked by a much larger (positive) paramagnetic susceptibility. The basic diamagnetism is independent of temperature and is due to the effect of applied magnetic fields on the motion of the inner electrons of the atoms present. The electronic orbits around the nuclei of atoms may often be considered as though they are an electric current. When a magnetic field is applied the electronic motions are modified and the magnetic moment due to the currents is changed. That is, there is an induced magnetic moment. Lenz's law of electromagnetic induction states that currents induced by a magnetic field are in such a direction that their magnetic fields tend to oppose the original inducing field. That is, the induced magnetization is negative, and so is the susceptibility. Mostly, this is one or two orders of magnitude weaker than paramagnetic susceptibilities and is only observed as a relatively minor correction which is usually independent of temperature.

An exception is the superconducting state, which is strongly diamagnetic and since a homogeneous type I superconductor is a perfect conductor it is perfectly diamagnetic. All magnetic induction is excluded from the specimen when an attempt is made to magnetize it from an unmagnetized state.

1.1.4 Antiferromagnetism

Antiferromagnetic materials are sometimes difficult to recognize superficially. In the simplest situation their paramagnetic state at relatively high temperatures follows a Curie-Weiss law with negative θ_p. There is a maximum in the susceptibility at the temperature, called the Néel temperature T_N, below which the material becomes antiferromagnetic. At lower temperatures the susceptibility usually decreases with decreasing temperature. The problem is that not all antiferromagnets show this maximum, although most simple ionic ones do. And a maximum in the susceptibility does not necessarily indicate antiferromagnetism. Metallic palladium (Fig. 3.1) shows a maximum at a temperature of about 80 K but it is not antiferromagnetic. The only conclusive proof of the antiferromagnetic state is obtained from neutron diffraction. Antiferromagnetism is discussed in Chapter 6.

1.1.5 Ferrimagnetism

Ferrimagnetic materials are superficially similar to ferromagnetics. They exhibit a spontaneous magnetic moment at temperatures below their Curie temperature T_C. Hysteresis and domain properties are observed in a similar way and they become paramagnetic at temperatures above T_C. One difference is that ferromagnetics are usually metallic and ferrimagnetics are unusually non-metals. But this is not an exclusive separation and it is not one based on the fundamental magnetism.

A more reliable difference that is observed experimentally is that the susceptibility of most ferromagnets measured above T_C follows the Curie-Weiss law reasonably well (at any rate within a few parts per hundred), but the susceptibility of most ferrimagnets does not follow this law until relatively high temperatures are reached. The graph of $1/\chi$ against T is often hyperbolic at temperatures up to about $2T_C$, becoming linear asymptotically (Fig. 1.10). At temperatures below T_C the temperature dependence of the spontaneous magnetization is often recognizably different from that for ferromagnets. A great variety of shapes of graphs of

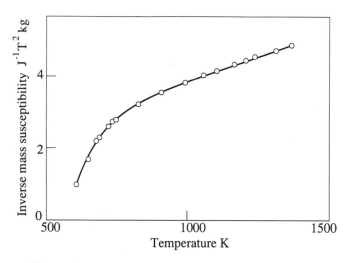

Figure 1.10 The reciprocal of the susceptibility of ferrimagnetic manganese ferrite $MnO.Fe_2O_3$ plotted against temperature.

spontaneous magnetization against temperature is found experimentally (see Fig. 6.9). Magnetic neutron diffraction gives a certain confirmation of a ferrimagnetic state. Many ferrimagnetic materials have very important technical applications. Ferrimagnetic properties are described in Chapter 6.

1.1.6 Helimagnetism and other non-collinear structures

Many materials exist in which the magnetic moments are ordered within a single domain (ferromagnetic, antiferromagnetic or ferrimagnetic) but they are not collinear. A group of these is helimagnetic materials. In the simplest form the moments lie in one crystallographic plane. The axis of the helix is normal to that plane. Moving from plane to plane along the axis the moment direction turns through a fixed angle from level to level, making a helix. Superficially this material looks like an antiferromagnet. The exact structure is known from neutron diffraction experiments. Other, more complicated, related structures exist: some non-collinear magnetic structures are very complicated.

1.2 Units in magnetism

It is important at this stage to consider the definition of units of the quantities that are commonly used in magnetism. The chief reason for this is to draw attention to the diversity of unit systems currently in use, and to try to provide a simple guide to conversion between the different systems.

In most areas of science and engineering, SI units have by now been adopted completely. The basic units are the metre, kilogram, second, ampere, kelvin (temperature), candela (luminous intensity) and the mole. There are numerous derived units. The system works well in many applications and it is widely accepted in teaching.

When polarizable media have to be considered the system is not uniquely defined and its advantages over the older, unrationalized cgs system are not obvious. The latter system is self-consistent and satisfactory and there has been a marked reluctance of workers in magnetism to change from cgs to SI units. Textbooks tend to be written in SI units and original work in magnetism is mostly in electromagnetic cgs units. The application of SI to magnetism can be contradictory and confusing. A vast amount of older information is firmly established in the cgs system. Research papers published currently in different countries are sometimes still in cgs units.

Since SI units are used almost everywhere else the case is strong that those working in magnetism should make the transition. Great care is still needed in the establishment of preferred SI units in magnetism so that conversion between the two systems shall be simple, straightforward and unambiguous. Translation factors involving multiples of 4π are to be avoided if at all possible. In this connection the SI definition of magnetic susceptibility needs special care.

The main differences of principle between the cgs and the SI systems applied to magnetism are:

1 In the SI system formulae dealing with force, energy, magnetic moment and so on are in terms of the induction B. The magnetic force H is rarely used alone. It only arises in calculating the magnetic effect of an electric current, or in similar cases. Whenever H interacts with any other quantity the permeability of free space μ_0 must be introduced. In free

space $B_0 = \mu_0 H$. The value of μ_0 is $4\pi \times 10^{-7}$ H m^{-1}. In the cgs system the formulae are in terms of the field strength H measured in oersteds. The permeability of free space is unity so that the induction (measured in gauss) in free space is numerically equal to the field.

In applying SI to magnetism there has seemed hitherto to be an arbitrary choice available between two alternatives. The Kennelly system (1936) was accepted first by electrical engineers. Physicists have been less ready to adopt it and various bodies have expressed a preference for the version proposed by Sommerfeld (1948). However, these two systems need not be contradictory or mutually exclusive.

2 The induction B in a polarizable medium is given in the SI system by $B = \mu_0(H + M) = B_0 + \mu_0 M$, where M is the magnetization per unit volume. This is the Sommerfeld system. In the Kennelly system $B = \mu_0 H + J$, where J is the magnetic polarization. There seems to be no reason why the Sommerfeld and the Kennelly systems should not both be employed, so long as there is a distinctive nomenclature. Whichever is the more convenient for a given situation should be used.

In the cgs system the induction in the medium is given by $B = H + 4\pi I$, where I is the magnetization per unit volume and is analogous to M.

The need to distinguish between the two kinds of induction, that which would be present in free space if the medium were absent and that actually present in the medium, has been a stumbling block in applying the SI system to magnetism. In this book the 'free space induction' $(= \mu_0 H)$ is given the symbol B_0 and called the field in SI. It is measured in tesla (T). H is measured in SI units of ampere metre^{-1}. It is currently used in electrical engineering but it is confusing where comparisons have to be made with fields measured in cgs units. B_0 can be used synonymously with the field H in cgs, so long as it is remembered that B_0 is really a free space induction. The induction in a medium is called the induction B in both systems.

Continuity at boundaries needs to be specified clearly. In cgs the normal component of the induction B and the tangential component of the field H are continuous across the boundary between different media. In SI there is no difference. The normal component of the induction B and the tangential component of the field $B_0 = \mu_0 H$ remain continuous at the boundary.

In many cases it is more satisfactory to standardize measurements against unit mass than against unit volume, since it is easier to measure mass accurately. The magnetization per unit mass $\sigma = M/\rho$, where ρ is the density (SI), or by $\sigma = I/\rho$ (cgs).

It is the definition of susceptibility in SI that causes most confusion. Different authors define susceptibility differently. In the Sommerfeld system the volume susceptibility is the magnetization divided by the field. In the Kennelly system it is the polarization divided by the field. But the question arises of how to define the field.

In this book we define the volume susceptibility in SI (Sommerfeld) as the ratio between the magnetization and the field B_0 which produces it.

$$\kappa = M/B_0 = M/(\mu_0 H)$$

This quantity is dimensionless and it is preferred because it converts easily with the cgs system.

The torque acting on a dipole in a field needs different handling in the Sommerfeld and Kennelly schemes, because of the different definitions of dipole moment. The Sommerfeld magnetization dipole moment is $m_s = VM$, where V is the volume of the specimen. The torque is $T = m_k \times H = VJ \times H = V\mu_0 M \times B_0/\mu_0$, since $J = \mu_0 M$ and $B_0 = \mu_0 H$. These results are clearly the same. The Sommerfeld scheme is usually more convenient for the physicist since H need never enter. The Bohr magneton is defined in this book as a Sommerfeld magnetization dipole moment. How it arises is described in Section 2.1.

The more common conversions of units between SI and cgs are given in Table 1.1.

Table 1.1 Units in magnetism

Quantity	SI	cgs(emu)
Permeability of free space	$\mu_0 = 4\pi \times 10^{-7}$ H m^{-1}	Unity
Induction in free space (field)	B_0 tesla (T)	B gauss (G)
Magnetic force (field)	H A m^{-1} 1 A m^{-1} = 0·01257 Oe	H oersted (Oe) 1 Oe = 79·58A m^{-1}
Induction in free space (field)	$B_0 = \mu_0 H$	$B = H$ 1 T equivalent to 10000 Oe
Induction in medium	$B = B_0 + M\mu_0$	$B = H + 4\pi I$ 1 T equal to 10000 G
Magnetization per unit volume	M J T^{-1}m^{-3} or A m^{-1}	I erg Oe^{-1}cm^{-3} 1000 J T^{-1}m^{-3} = 1 erg Oe^{-1}cm^{-3}
Magnetization per unit mass	$\sigma = M/\rho$ J T^{-1}kg^{-1}	$\sigma = I/\rho$ erg Oe^{-1}g^{-1} where ρ = density
Magnetic polarization	J (in T) $B = B_0 + J$	$4\pi I$ (in G) $B = H + 4\pi I$
Sommerfeld magnetization dipole moment	$m_s = V M$	
Kennelly polarization dipole moment	$m_k = V J$	where V = volume
Susceptibility per unit volume	$\kappa = M/B_0$ J T^{-2}m^{-3}	$\kappa = I/H$ erg Oe^{-2}cm^{-3} 10 J T^{-2}m^{-3} = 10^{-6} erg Oe^{-2}cm^{-3}
Susceptibility per unit mass	$\chi = \kappa/\rho$ J T^{-2}kg^{-1}	$\chi = \kappa/\rho$ erg Oe^{-2}g^{-1} 10^{-2} J T^{-2}kg^{-1} = 10^{-6} erg Oe^{-2}g^{-1}
Susceptibility per mole	χ_M J T^{-2}mole^{-1}	
Force on ferromagnetic specimen	$F_z = m\sigma \, dB_0/dz$	
Force on paramagnetic specimen	$F_z = m\chi \, B_0 \, dB_0/dz$	
Bohr magneton	$\mu_B = eh/4\pi m$ = 9·2732 × 10^{-24}J T^{-1}	= 9·2732 × 10^{-21}erg Oe^{-1}
Relative permeability	$\mu = B/B_0 = 1 + \mu_0\kappa$	$\mu = B/H = 1 + 4\pi\kappa$ same value in both systems
Torque	$T = VM\times B_0$ (Sommerfeld) $T = V J \times H$ (Kennelly)	$T = V I \times H$
Demagnetizing field	$(B_0)_D = DM$ $D = \mu_0 N/4\pi$	$(H)_D = NI$
Energy of a permanent magnet Energy product	$(B_0 B)_{max}$ J m^{-3}	$(BH)_{max}$ 1 MG Oe = 7·958 kJ m^{-3}

Chapter 2 _____

Localized magnetism associated with the ion cores

2.1 The origins of the magnetic properties of materials

Magnetism arises from the motion of electrons, the quantized nature of which gives rise to the fundamental unit of magnetic dipole moment, the Bohr magneton μ_B, which arises as follows.

The dipole moment associated with a loop of electric current I is IA, where A is the area of the loop. If the current consists of an electron of charge e and mass m rotating in a circular orbit of radius r at angular velocity ω, the magnetic dipole moment

$$\mu = IA = -\tfrac{1}{2}er \times v = -e(\omega/2\pi)\pi r^2 = -\tfrac{1}{2}e\omega r^2$$

The angular momentum

$$= |J| = m|r \times v| = m\omega r^2$$

That is,

$$\mu = -(e/2m)J$$

$$J = \frac{h}{2\pi}$$

The angular momentum is quantized in units of $h/2\pi$, where h is the Planck constant. The lowest non-zero value for μ is $\mu_B = eh/4\pi m$. Its value is $9\cdot2741 \times 10^{-24}\,\mathrm{J\,T^{-1}}$ (SI), or $9\cdot2741 \times 10^{-21}\,\mathrm{erg\,Oe^{-1}}$ (cgs).

This treatment is for the special case of a simple electron orbit. More generally (and including the case of electron spin) $\mu = \gamma J$, where γ is called the magnetomechanical ratio. For pure orbital motion of an electron $\gamma = -e/2m$. For pure electron spin $\gamma = -e/m$.

2.2 The magnetic moment of a single free ion

The magnetic properties of solid materials are determined fundamentally by the characteristics of the individual atoms present, and by the electrons associated with these atoms. In trying to understand the properties that are observed experimentally, we are concerned with the way in which all the atoms and electrons in the solid interact to give the whole effect.

Four quantum numbers, n, l, m_l and m_s are required to describe the state of an electron in an atom. A given electron shell, defined by electrons all having the same principal quantum number n, is full when it contains $2n^2$ electrons. Transitions between different n levels do not concern us in considering the magnetic properties of solids, because the energy differences involved (known from their atomic spectra) are too great, being of the order of 10^5 cm^{-1}. The cm^{-1} is a convenient, though arbitrary, unit of energy.

1 cm^{-1} is 1/8066 eV, or 1.98×10^{-23} J

l can take the values 0, 1, 2, . . . $(n-1)$

The magnetic quantum number m_l has $(2l+1)$ possible values,

$-l, (-l+1), \ldots 0, \ldots (l-1), l$

The spin quantum number s is 1/2 and $m_s = \pm 1/2$

Thus for any allowed value of l there are $2(2l+1)$ levels. l values are usually indicated by a convention used originally in spectroscopy.

symbol	s p d f g h . . .
l	0 1 2 3 4 5 . . .

In the first transition series of elements the magnetism arises from d-electrons $(l=2)$. In rare earths it comes from f-electrons $(l=3)$.

How the electrons combine in an atom to produce a stable state of least energy (the ground state) is determined partly by the relative magnitudes of the energies of interaction of the following types. The vectors $l_{i,k}$ and $s_{i,k}$ represent respectively the orbital and the spin angular moments of the ith and the kth electrons in the atom.

$a_{ik}l_i \cdot s_k$ is the spin–orbit interaction, either for the interaction between the orbital angular momentum of one electron and its own spin $(i = k)$ or between different electrons;

$b_{ik}l_i \cdot l_k$ is the orbit–orbit interaction between different electrons;

$c_{ik}s_i \cdot s_k$ is the spin–spin interaction between different electrons.

For the spin–orbit interaction, the orbital angular momentum of a given electron interacts more strongly with its own spin than with the spins of other electrons and $|a_{ii}| \gg |a_{ik}|$. The dominant mechanism in determining a_{ii} is the coupling between l_i and s_i through the interaction of both with the nuclear charge. a_{ii} is largest for heavy atoms with high atomic number.

If the constants a, b and c are all of the same order of magnitude, the problem of the energy and nature of the electronic motion becomes complex. It is found experimentally that in most cases, except for the heaviest elements, the spin–orbit constants a_{ii} and a_{ik} are small compared with b_{ik} and c_{ik}. The spins form a resultant vector S for the whole atom and the orbital moments form a resultant L. The corresponding atomic quantum numbers are S and L. The spin–orbit interaction can then be regarded as a relatively small (but not usually zero) coupling between L and S. When external influences are not too strong, S and L are combined into a resultant vector J. The corresponding quantum number J can take the values

$$J = |L - S|, |L - S + 1|, \ldots |L + S - 1|, |L + S|$$

It should be remembered that while we deal here with these vectors in a simple geometrical way, in a fuller quantum mechanical treatment they are matrices. The application of a notional very small magnetic field defines a direction of quantization. The projection M_J of J in the direction of quantization is also quantized and $M_J = -J, (-J + 1), \ldots (J - 1), J$.

In a given atom the maximum values of L and S are given by Σl_i and Σs_i respectively but other values can occur between the limits of $\Sigma \pm l_i$ and $\Sigma \pm s$ given by Σm_l and Σm_s. The choice of L and S is made by applying Hund's rules. These are essentially empirical, and first arose in interpreting atomic spectra.

2.2.1 Hund's rules

(1) The combination of s_i that gives the lowest energy (i.e. is the most stable) is that with the highest value of $(2S + 1)$.

(2) If when the first rule has been satisfied there are several possible L values all having the same value of $(2S + 1)$, that with the largest L will be the most stable.

Hund's rules have full theoretical justification only in very limited cases; but there is little doubt of their validity, at any rate for the lighter elements. The argument to support them is as follows.

(1) Dual occupation of a spatial electron distribution (two electrons of opposite spin in one orbital) must involve large electrostatic electron–electron repulsions because of the proximity of the two electrons. Energy is lowered if dual occupations are minimized, giving as many like spins as possible. The operation of this rule leads directly to the possession of relatively large magnetic moments by partially filled d- and f-electron shells, in transition elements and rare earths.

(2) Having satisfied the first condition, if the electrons orbit in the same sense (that is, where l_i has the same sign) electron–electron repulsive interactions are minimized because the electrons spend more of the time further apart. Under this condition L takes the largest value compatible with the configuration and with the first condition.

The energies associated with rule (1) are of a larger order of magnitude than those associated with the second rule.

The following examples illustrate the application of the rules.

(a) Co^{2+} ion, in a $3d^7$ state. For 3d electrons $l_i = 2$

m_s	1/2	1/2	1/2	1/2	1/2	-1/2	-1/2	-1/2	-1/2	-1/2
m_l	2	1	0	-1	-2	2	1	0	-1	-2

Counting the seven electrons from the left we have

$S = 3/2; (2S+1) = 4; L = 3$

(b) Dy^{3+} ion, in a $4f^9$ state. For 4f electrons $l_i = 3$

m_s	1/2	1/2	1/2	1/2	1/2	1/2	1/2	-1/2	-1/2	-1/2	-1/2	-1/2	-1/2	-1/2
m_l	3	2	1	0	-1	-2	-3	3	2	1	0	-1	-2	-3

Counting the nine electrons from the left we have

$S = 5/2; 2S+1 = 6; L = 5$

2.2.2 Combination of L and S to form J

If there were no spin–orbit interaction all the $(2S+1)$ (when L exceeds S) or $(2L+1)$ (when S exceeds L) possible values of J (multiplets) would correspond to the same energy. In general this is not so, because of energy differences provided by spin–orbit interaction. The multiplets are split, as follows.

By analogy with the previous (electronic) case the atomic spin–orbit coupling energy is written as

$W_J = AL.S$

The constant A is the atomic spin–orbit interaction coefficient. It is related to some combination of the individual electronic constants a_{ik} and is expected to be dominated by the interaction of spins with their own orbital moments. We may regard it as a quantity known from experiment. It is positive when the electron shell is less than half full and negative when it is more than half full. If we write

$J^2 = (L+S)^2 = L^2 + S^2 + 2L.S$ then

$W_J = 1/2 A (J^2 - L^2 - S^2)$

When A is positive, W_J is least when J (and therefore J) is least. $J = |L - S|$ gives the lowest energy and $J = |L + S|$ gives the highest, and *vice versa* when A is negative. When an electron shell is less than half full the most stable multiplet component is $J = |L-S|$. When it is more than half full the multiplets are inverted and the most stable component is $J = |L+S|$. At the half-way point $L = 0$ and $J = S$. When the shell is filled completely L, S and J are all zero and the shell is magnetically inert, except for a weak diamagnetic contribution. The range of energy between the lowest and highest multiplets is

$$|A/2\{J(J+1)_{max} - J(J+1)_{min}\}|$$

For Co^{2+} A is -180 cm^{-1} and the energy range is 1890 cm^{-1}.

Each multiplet state (J) contains $(2J+1)$ sub-states, or levels, corresponding to the different allowed values of M_J. In the free atom, when no external fields are applied, all the levels of a given state have the same energy. Applying a magnetic field separates the energies of the levels and removes the degeneracy. The occupation of these levels in the equilibrium (or ground) state is governed by the laws of statistical mechanics.

Most of the fundamental magnetic properties of materials stem from changes in the total energy as atoms are redistributed among the levels when magnetic fields are applied, or when the temperature is changed. A state for which $J = 0$ (or $2J+1 = 1$) cannot produce a magnetic moment, because no change in distribution (or energy) can take place under the influence of a field. Figure 2.1 illustrates the scheme of energy levels for the Co^{2+} ion in the free state.

The quantum numbers of a multiplet state are often written in spectroscopic notation in the form $^{2S+1}L_J$, or for a sub-level of this state $^{2S+1}L_J{}^{M_J}$

L values are given by the symbols

symbol	S	P	D	F	G	H	...
L	0	1	2	3	4	5	...

Thus for the two examples given previously, Co^{2+} is in the $^4F_{9/2}$ state (for which there are ten M_J sub-levels) and Dy^{3+} is in the $^6H_{15/2}$ state (sixteen sub-levels).

2.2.3 Units of magnetic moment

In connecting the quantum numbers L, S and J with the angular momentum vectors $\boldsymbol{L}$, $\boldsymbol{S}$ and $\boldsymbol{J}$ we write, for the general case

$$\boldsymbol{L}^2 = L(L+1)(h/2\pi)^2$$
$$\boldsymbol{S}^2 = S(S+1)(h/2\pi)^2$$
$$\boldsymbol{J}^2 = J(J+1)(h/2\pi)^2$$

The reason for this particular form is connected with the fact that we deal with the sum of three Cartesian components of the angular moments and these angular moments are really matrices. In contrast, the projection

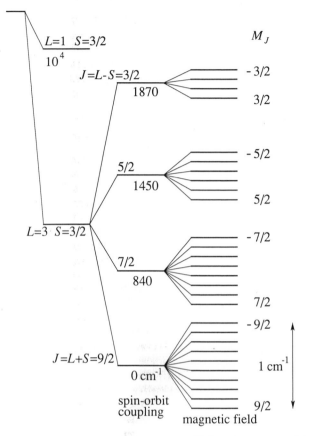

Figure 2.1 Energy levels of the cobalt free ion Co^{2+} (not drawn to scale). Energies are in cm^{-1}, where $8066\ cm^{-1} = 1\ eV$.

of the total angular momentum J in the single quantization direction is given by $M_J(h/2\pi)$.

The corresponding magnetic moment vectors are

$$\boldsymbol{\mu}_L = \mu_B\{L(L+1)\}^{1/2} \tag{2.1}$$

$$\boldsymbol{\mu}_S = 2\mu_B\{S(S+1)\}^{1/2} \tag{2.2}$$

and $\boldsymbol{\mu}_J$, where μ_B is the Bohr magneton.

Because of spin–orbit interaction, the resultant vectors L and S for the whole atom may be regarded as precessing about their vector sum J. This is based on a quantum–mechanical result that while L and S may have finite derivatives with respect to time, their sum $J = L + S$ may not. The associated magnetic moment precesses accordingly around the direction of J but there is a complication because the factor two appears on the right-hand side of the equation for the spin magnetic moment, but not in the equivalent expression for the spin angular momentum.

The resultant magnetic moment $\boldsymbol{\mu} = \boldsymbol{\mu}_L + \boldsymbol{\mu}_S$ (precessing about J) may be resolved into a time-independent part $\boldsymbol{\mu}_J$ along the $\boldsymbol{J}$ direction and a high frequency part $\boldsymbol{\mu}'$ perpendicular to $\boldsymbol{J}$ which depends on time, the long-time average of which is zero.

$$\boldsymbol{\mu} = \boldsymbol{\mu}_J + \boldsymbol{\mu}'$$

The quantities $\boldsymbol{\mu}_J$ and $\boldsymbol{\mu}'$ are roughly equivalent respectively to a fixed dipole moment and to a polarization effect. Here we consider the predominant time-independent part only.

From Figure 2.2

$$\mu_J^2 = [(2\pi/h)\mu_B]^2(L.J/|J| + 2S.J/|J|)^2$$

Since

$$S^2 = (J-L)^2 = J^2 + L^2 - 2L.J$$

then

$$L.J = 1/2(J^2 + L^2 - S^2)$$

and similarly

$$S.J = 1/2(J^2 + S^2 - L^2)$$

That is

$$\mu_J^2 = (2\pi/h\mu_B)^2\left(\frac{3J^2 + S^2 - L^2}{2|J|^2}\right)^2 J^2$$

$$= \mu_B^2\left(\frac{3J(J+1) + S(S+1) - L(L+1)}{2J(J+1)}\right)^2 J(J+1) \qquad (2.3)$$

or,

$$\mu_J = g\mu_B\{J(J+1)\}^{1/2} \qquad (2.4)$$

$$\text{where } g = 1 + \frac{J(J+1) + S(S+1) - L(L+1)}{2J(J+1)} \qquad (2.5)$$

is the Landé g-factor and has the value 2 when $L = 0$ and the value 1 when $S = 0$.

This defines the magnetic moment of a single atom. In the absence of an applied field all atoms having the same moment have the same energy. When a magnetic field B_0 is applied, the energy depends on the statistical occupation of the $(2J+1)$ sub-levels, all of which differ in their M_J value.

The magnetic energy of a given atom is

$$E_M = -\boldsymbol{\mu}_J.B_0 = -g\mu_B M_J B_0$$

This is usually in the range 0·1 to 10 cm^{-1}, for applied fields of the order of 1 T (10^4 Oe). At a temperature of 300 K the thermal energy kT is 209 cm^{-1}.

The magnetic sub-levels are occupied according to the laws of statistical

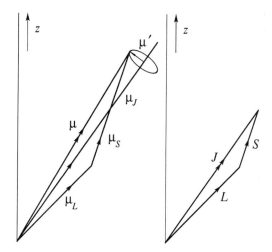

Figure 2.2 Vector atom model.

mechanics, the lowest energy having the largest population. The relative population P of a sub-level M_J is

$$P(M_J) = \frac{\exp(-E_M/kT)}{\sum \exp(-E_M/kT)} \qquad \text{(Note: } E_M \text{ is negative)}$$

2.3 Magnetic moment of an assembly of atoms, without interactions

The total magnetic moment of the whole can now be added up, taking the populations of the sub-levels into account. Usually the spacing of the multiplet levels is very large compared with the splitting of the magnetic sub-levels, with no inter-mixing of multiplets. We assume that to be the case here.

The mean magnetic moment in the field direction is

$$\langle \mu_{J\uparrow} \rangle = \sum_{M_J} g\mu_B M_J P(M_J)$$

or,

$$\frac{\langle \mu_{J\uparrow} \rangle}{(g\mu_B)} = \frac{\sum M_J \exp(g\mu_B M_J B_0/kT)}{\sum_{M_J} \exp(g\mu_B M_J B_0/kT)}$$

Where each of the summations is over all the M_J sub-levels.

In order to evaluate this expression we write

$$u = \ln(\Sigma \exp(M_J y/J)) = \ln(v)$$

where $y = Jg\mu_B B_0/kT$

and $v = \Sigma \exp(M_J y/J)$

Then $\dfrac{du}{dy} = \dfrac{du}{dv} \cdot \dfrac{dv}{dy} = \dfrac{\Sigma (M_J/J) \exp\{M_J y/J\}}{\Sigma \exp\{M_J y/J\}} = \dfrac{\langle \mu_{J\uparrow} \rangle}{Jg\mu_B}$

The problem is now to evaluate the sum

$$v = \sum_{-J}^{+J} \exp(M_J y/J)$$

This may be seen as the sum of a simple geometric progression as follows.

Let $z = \exp(y/J)$, so that $\exp(M_J y/J) = z^{M_J}$

Then

$$v = \sum_{-J}^{+J} z^{M_J} = z^{-J}(1 + z + z^2 + \ldots + z^{2J})$$

$$= \frac{z^{-J}(z^{(2J+1)} - 1)}{z - 1} = \frac{z^{(J+1/2)} - z^{-(J+1/2)})}{z^{1/2} - z^{-1/2}}$$

$$\frac{\exp\{(1+1/2J)y\} - \exp\{-(1+1/2J)y\}}{\exp(y/2J) - \exp(-y/2J)} = \frac{\sinh(1+1/2J)y}{\sinh(y/2J)}$$

and

$$\frac{dv}{dy} = \frac{\begin{array}{c}(1+1/2J)\{\sinh(y/2J).\cosh(1+1/2J)y\} \\ -1/2J\{\sinh(1+1/2J)y.\cosh(y/2J)\}\end{array}}{[(\sinh(y/2J)]^2}$$

Also,

$$\frac{du}{dv} = \frac{1}{v}$$

Thus,

$$du/dy = (du/dv)(dv/dy) = \langle \mu_{J\uparrow} \rangle/Jg\mu_B$$
$$= (1+1/2J)\coth\{(1+1/2J)y\} - 1/2J\coth(y/2J)$$
$$= F(J,y) \text{ where } y = Jg\mu_B B_0/kT$$

$F(J,y)$ is known as the Brillouin function. It is shown in Figure 2.3 as a function of y, for selected values of J. In the special (but common) case when $J = 1/2$

$$F(J,y) = 2\coth 2y - \coth y = \tanh y \qquad (2.6)$$

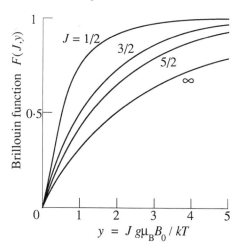

Figure 2.3 Brillouin function for different values of J.

The other notable case is the classical one where there is a continuous range of orientations of J. That is when $(2J+1) = \infty$, and $J = \infty$. This applies to the phenomenon of superparamagnetism, referred to later.

The saturation value (for large y) is where $F(J,y) = 1$, and all the atomic moments are aligned in the field direction. This condition is normally reached only in ferromagnetics but it has been observed in strong fields and at low temperatures in some paramagnetics, as shown in Figure 2.4.

2.4 Paramagnetic susceptibility of an array of atoms

Observations are usually made on paramagnetic materials under the condition of small y; that is, near the origin of the Brillouin function. The paramagnetic susceptibility is related to the initial slope of the Brillouin curve.

When x is small, $\coth x = 1/x + x/3$

That is, for small y,

$$F(J,y) = 1/y + y/3(1+1/2J)^2 - 1/y - y/3(1/2J)^2$$
$$= y(J+1)/3J$$

In one mole there are N atoms. The total magnetic moment per mole is

$$N\langle \mu_{J\uparrow} \rangle = NJg\mu_B F(J,y)$$
$$= Ng^2\mu_B^2 J(J+1)B_0/3kT$$

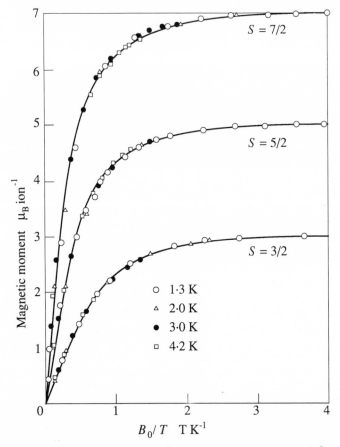

Figure 2.4 Paramagnetic saturation in salts containing the ions $Gd^{3+}(S = 7/2)$, $Fe^{3+}(S = 5/2)$ and $Cr^{3+}(S = 3/2)$. The magnetic moment is plotted against the ratio of field to temperature (after Henry, 1952, Phys. Rev., **88**, 559).

The susceptibility per mole

$$\chi_M = \text{moment}/B_0$$

$$\frac{\text{moment}}{B_0} = g^2 J(J+1) \frac{N\mu_B^2}{3kT} = p_{\text{eff}}^2 \frac{N\mu_B^2}{3kT} \tag{2.7}$$

$p_{\text{eff}} = g\{J(J+1)\}^{1/2}$ is a useful quantity for comparing the properties of different materials, and is easy to measure experimentally. It is called the effective paramagnetic Bohr magneton number.

It is found by experiment that for many materials the Curie law

$$\chi_M = C_M T^{-1} \text{ is obeyed, where } C_M \text{ is the molar Curie constant.}$$

Thus

$$p_{eff}^2 = \frac{3k}{N\mu_B^2}\, C_M \simeq 0.8 C_M \text{ (in SI units), or} \simeq 8 C_M \text{ (in cgs units).}$$

A fuller treatment of the paramagnetism of free ions gives the result

$$\chi_M = p_{eff}^2 N\mu_B^2 / 3kT + \alpha_J$$

The term α_J derives from the high-frequency part $\boldsymbol{\mu}'$ of the magnetic moment of an atom. It is independent of temperature and in very many cases it is so small compared with the first term that its effect cannot be observed. α_J makes a significant contribution only if the multiplet separation is not large compared with kT.

2.5 Comparison with experiment

The first point to mention is that the law often found experimentally is of the form $\chi = C_M(T - \theta)^{-1}$. This is the Curie-Weiss law, which will be discussed later. The modification arises because in many materials the atomic magnetic moments are not non-interacting. The relationship between C_M and p_{eff} is not affected.

2.5.1 Experimental behaviour of rare earth salts and metals

Many salts and other compounds of the rare earth elements are paramagnetic and at appropriate temperatures their susceptibility follows a Curie-Weiss law $\chi = C_M(T - \theta)^{-1}$. Values of p_{eff} derived from measurements on different salts of the same ion generally agree well. Also, the susceptibility of most of the pure rare earth metals measured at relatively high temperatures follows the Curie-Weiss law (Fig. 2.5) and the respec-

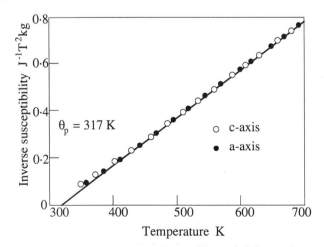

Figure 2.5 Reciprocal susceptibility of metallic gadolinium above the Curie temperature (after Nigh, Legvold and Spedding, 1963, Phys. Rev., **132**, 1092).

tive values of p_{eff} are similar to those of the salts. Experimental values of p_{eff} are compared with those calculated from the simple theory in Figure 2.6, which mostly shows good agreement.

This agreement indicates that the magnetic electrons in the rare earth atoms or ions are relatively little affected by external influences. The 4f electrons are deep in the atoms and are fairly well screened from intra-crystalline electric fields by a significant outer electron distribution which includes the 5s and 5p closed shells. The radial charge distributions of the various atomic electron levels calculated for Gd^{3+} ions are shown in Figure 2.7.

The most obvious discrepancies shown in Figure 2.6 are for samarium and europium. The reason for the disagreements is that for these two elements the multiplet intervals cannot be regarded as infinitely large compared with kT. The multiplet spacings are shown in Figure 2.8.

When the intervals are comparable to kT account must be taken of statistical occupation of higher multiplets and their magnetic sub-levels. The treatment is more complicated than the wide-multiplet case but it is similar in principle. The result is to give for Sm^{3+} and Eu^{3+} susceptibility values that do not follow a simple Curie-Weiss law but that do agree well with experiment. In the absence of this effect Eu^{3+} would have a paramagnetic susceptibility of zero, having a singlet ground state $J = 0$. This is a case where the term α_J mentioned in Section 2.4 does contribute significantly.

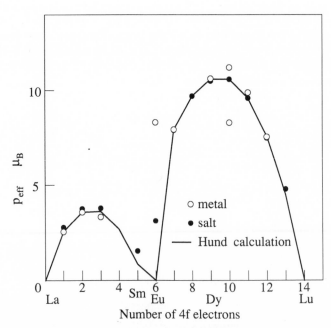

Figure 2.6 Experimental and calculated values of p_{eff} for rare earths.

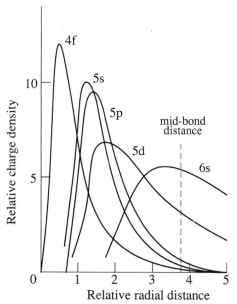

Figure 2.7 The radial distribution of atomic electrons in gadolinium (after Freeman and Watson, 1962, Phys. Rev., **127**, 2058).

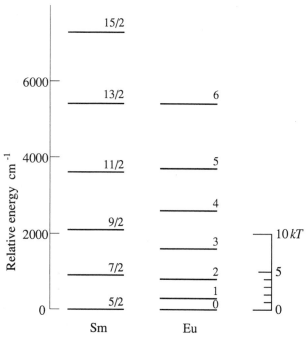

Figure 2.8 Multiplet spacings of Sm^{3+} and Eu^{3+}. The scale showing thermal energy is for a temperature of 300 K and the numbers on the levels are the J values.

2.5.2 Experimental behaviour of transition series salts

The experimental susceptibility of metallic transition metals does not support the free ion theory at all. This is because the magnetic d-electrons are also involved to a varying degree in crystal bonding and conduction and the free ion model is not appropriate. For salts of the first transition series of elements, the agreement with the simple free ion theory is mostly rather poor. However, if it is assumed that orbital moment plays no part in the magnetism and that the moment is wholly from spin, experimental and calculated values of p_{eff} agree quite well for many of these salts (see Fig. 2.9).

The value for p_{eff} then becomes $p_{\mathrm{eff}} = 2\{S(S+1)\}^{1/2}$, since when $L = 0$, g has the value 2.

The reason for this loss of orbital moment is that the magnetic electrons in transition series ions are not screened. The partly filled 3d shells feel the effect of anisotropic crystalline electric fields produced by their environment. In the first transition series the effects of crystal field are stronger than those of spin–orbit coupling, although not so strong as to break down the couplings which operate in isolated atoms to set up the resultant vectors S and L. This contrasts with the behaviour of rare earth ions, where the spin–orbit coupling is stronger than the crystal field effects.

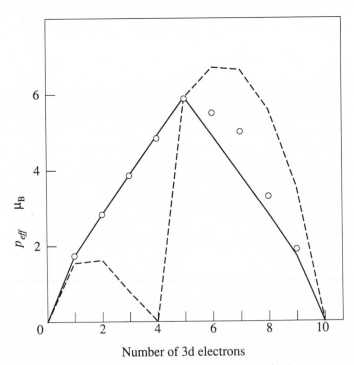

Figure 2.9 Experimental values (O) of p_{eff} for ions of the first transition series. Calculated values, --- for full J, —— for S only.

2.5.3 Crystal field effects

The crystal field exerts its greatest influence on the direction of the orbital angular momentum. It does not interact directly with electron spin. In an atom, differing values of the atomic quantum numbers L and M_L correspond to different spatial distributions of electronic charge, and when L is not equal to zero these are not spherically symmetrical. They spread out in various directions in the form of lobes and other shapes. In the free atom, when no magnetic field is applied, there is no reason to distinguish between the directions of the different orbital distributions. In a solid crystal other ions surround the atom in question and set up an electrostatic field. Those lobes of charge which point towards neighbouring atoms (regarded as point charges) correspond to higher energies than those which point between atoms. What in free space would be a degenerate situation involving different M_L states is split in the crystal into different energy levels, widely enough separated to be immune from thermal excitation at modest temperatures. The detailed pattern of splitting depends on the symmetry of the crystal and not all the orbital degeneracy is necessarily removed. Lower symmetry generally leads to more splitting. The mean values of the components of the orbital momentum in the three cartesian directions average out to zero. When a magnetic field is applied the components still have mean values that are zero and there is no orbital contribution to the whole magnetic moment. This is known as quenching of the orbital magnetic moment. When the orbital moment is totally quenched only spin moment contributes.

The crystal field effects in salts of the elements of the first transition series produce energy intervals of the order of $10^4 \, \text{cm}^{-1}$. The much weaker spin–orbit coupling then acts as a small perturbation, resulting in a weak polarization of the orbital wave functions. This causes the mean value of the orbital momentum no longer to be exactly zero and produces a small contribution to the magnetic moment. The g-factor differs from the spin-only value of two; and this gives the mechanism whereby a mainly spin-type magnetic moment is coupled with the directionality of the crystal. This effect is known as magnetocrystalline anisotropy. It has important technological consequences.

Sometimes the orbital moment is not completely quenched and a degenerate orbital ground state remains. This is acted upon and split by spin–orbit coupling energy kT. The observed susceptibility then deviates from the Curie (or Curie-Weiss) law at relatively low temperatures, tending to approach the law at high temperatures.

2.5.4 Direct measurement of the g-factor

At the beginning of this chapter, reference was made to the magnetomechanical ratio γ, and values were given for pure orbital motion and for pure electron spin. More generally,

$$\gamma = -(e/2m)g$$

and direct measurement of γ can lead to experimental values for g which may be compared with the values predicted by application of Hund's rules.

The direct experiment to measure γ in paramagnetic materials consists of applying a magnetic field to a specimen of the solid containing the magnetic ions and then measuring the gross change in angular momentum of the whole specimen produced by the magnetomechanical interaction of the electrons. The experiment was carried out for a number of rare earth and first transition series paramagnetic compounds by Sucksmith between 1930 and 1932.

A resonance method was used in which the specimen was suspended and acted upon by a slowly alternating magnetic field which had a frequency equal to the natural frequency of the suspended system. Values of γ and therefore of g were derived from the amplitude of the oscillation produced. This was one of the most delicate and skilful experiments ever carried out in magnetism.

Table 2.1 Magnetomechanical measurements of g-factor

Material	Paramagnetic ion	Ground state	Calculated g		Experimental g
			Full J	Spin only	
Rare earths					
Nd_2O_3	Nd^{3+}	$^4I_{5/2}$	0·73		0·78
Gd_2O_3	Gd^{3+}	$^8S_{7/2}$	2·00		2·12
Dy_2O_3	Dy^{3+}	$^6H_{15/2}$	1·33		1·36
First transition series					
$CrCl_3$	Cr^{3+}	$^4F_{3/2}$	0·40	2·00	1·95
$MnSO_4$	Mn^{2+}	$^6S_{5/2}$	2·00	2·00	1·98
$FeSO_4$	Fe^{2+}	$^5D_4$	1·50	2·00	1·89
$CoSO_4$	Co^{2+}	$^4F_{9/2}$	1·33	2·00	1·54

The results (see Table 2.1) confirmed the predictions of the Hund theory for rare earths and showed that indeed spin moment is dominant for ions of the first transition series.

Complementary measurements using microwave resonance techniques have been made more recently. They support the same conclusions.

2.6 Ferromagnetism in the local moment model, with interactions

A ferromagnetic sample is usually divided up into domains which are spontaneously strongly magnetized. Applied magnetic fields can change the direction of the magnetization within the domains but except in certain circumstances they make little difference to its magnitude. The magnetization within the domain is called the intrinsic magnetization $\sigma_{B,T}$ (per unit mass at temperature T) and its value in zero field is the spontaneous magnetization $\sigma_{0,T}$. The saturation magnetization $\sigma_{0,0}$ is the value of $\sigma_{0,T}$ at zero temperature.

A basic explanation of the occurrence of the spontaneous magnetization was derived from the postulate put forward by Weiss in 1907 that an intense internal or molecular magnetic field exists within the ferromagnetic solid. This was assumed to act upon each atomic magnetic moment and to be proportional in magnitude to the magnetization of the part of the solid immediately surrounding the moment in question. The magnitude of this field was typically of the order of 10^3 T (or 10^7 Oe).

Weiss realized that such a strong field could not be provided by purely magnetic effects such as dipole fields. It is now recognized as being a convenient way of treating interatomic interaction effects, which can be represented as though they are equivalent to an internal magnetic field. While the Weiss model in its simplest form was very successful in explaining the existence of a ferromagnetic state, it is known now that the materials to which it was first applied (metallic iron, nickel and cobalt) are not good examples of ionic ferromagnets. Their magnetism is not strongly localized in the ion cores. The rare earth elements are better examples.

The justification for the assumption that the molecular field is proportional to the local magnetization is the expectation that the driving force tending to align an atomic moment in the same direction as that of its neighbourhood will depend on what proportion of its neighbours are already aligned. The magnetization of the neighbourhood is a measure of this.

What was called the applied field B_0 in the treatment of ionic paramagnetism now becomes the sum of the internal and the applied fields

$$= (B_0)_i + B_0$$

If N_s is the number of atoms per kg of specimen ($= 1000\, N/M$, where N the Avogadro number and M is the molar weight of the substance), the intrinsic magnetization per unit mass

$$\sigma_{B,T} = N_s \langle \mu_{J\uparrow} \rangle$$

We write $(B_0)_i = \gamma_m \sigma_{B,T} = N_s \gamma_m \langle \mu_{J\uparrow} \rangle$ where γ_m is a constant of proportionality called the molecular field coefficient.

2.6.1 Calculation of the spontaneous magnetization

We now include the molecular field in the theory given already for the paramagnetic case. The quantity abbreviated as y becomes

$$y' = Jg\mu_B(B_0 + N_s\gamma_m \langle \mu_{J\uparrow} \rangle)/kT \text{ and we look again for a solution for } \langle \mu_{J\uparrow} \rangle.$$

As before, but writing y' for y

$$\langle \mu_{J\uparrow} \rangle / Jg\mu_B = \sigma_{B,T}/\sigma_{0,0} = F(J, y') \tag{2.8}$$

Now the solution is less obvious than before, since $\langle \mu_{J\uparrow} \rangle$ appears on both sides of the equation. When we deal with the spontaneous magnetization $\sigma_{0,T}$ we mean that the applied field B_0 is zero. That is,

$$y' = Jg\mu_B N_s \gamma_m \langle \mu_{J\uparrow} \rangle / kT$$

$$\text{or, } \langle \mu_{J\uparrow} \rangle / Jg\mu_B = \sigma_{0,T}/\sigma_{0,0} = [kT/N_s\gamma_m(Jg\mu_B)^2]y' \qquad (2.9)$$

The curves of the Equations (2.8) and (2.9) are shown in Figure 2.10. The solution sought is clearly the non-zero intersection of lines (1) and (2).

The position of curve (1) is independent of temperature. The slope of curve (2) is proportional to T. As the slope of curve (2) increases with rising temperature, the solution for the reduced magnetization represented by the ordinate of the intersection decreases and becomes zero when the slope of curve (2) exceeds the initial slope of curve (1). The temperature at which the magnetization becomes zero is the ferromagnetic Curie temperature T_C.

The calculated variation of the reduced spontaneous magnetization with temperature is shown in Figure 2.11. The exact form of the curve depends on J. The result agrees roughly with experiment, but this is not a very sensitive test of the theory.

Similarly the calculation may be extended to give the expected dependence of intrinsic magnetization on field at different temperatures. Finite values of B_0 are included so that Equation (2.9) becomes

$$\langle \mu_{J\uparrow} \rangle / Jg\mu_B = ATy' - C \qquad (2.10)$$

where $A = k/[N_s\gamma_m(Jg\mu_B)^2]$

and $C = B_0/[N_s\gamma_m Jg\mu_B]$

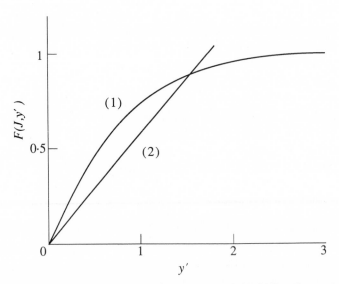

Figure 2.10 Solution of Equations (2.8) (line 1) and (2.9) (line 2) to calculate the spontaneous magnetization of a ferromagnet.

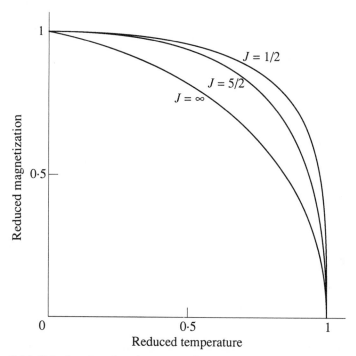

Figure 2.11 Calculated reduced curves of spontaneous magnetization plotted against temperature.

Simultaneous solution of Equations (2.8) and (2.10) gives values of intrinsic magnetization for varying field at chosen fixed temperatures, as shown in Figure 2.12. This is broadly similar to experiment (Figs. 1.3 and 4.13) but the detailed agreement is not good for metallic ferromagnets.

2.6.2 Relationship between the molecular field coefficient and the Curie temperature

Since the existence of a ferromagnetic state depends on the magnetic interactions represented by the molecular field, it is to be expected that a close relationship will exist between the molecular field coefficient γ_m and the Curie temperature T_C at which the ferromagnetic state breaks down. When no field is applied and at temperatures immediately below T_C the magnetization and therefore y' are small. The approximate form of the Brillouin function may be used.

$$F(J, y') = \sigma_{0,T}/\sigma_{0,0} = (J+1)y'/3J$$

Also (Equation (2.9) above)

$$\sigma_{0,T}/\sigma_{0,0} = kTy'/N_s\gamma_m(Jg\mu_B)^2$$

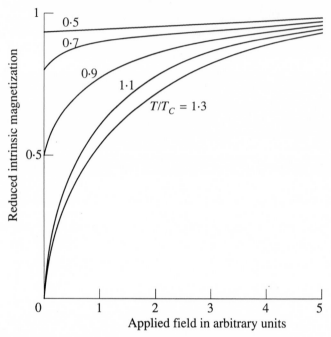

Figure 2.12 Calculated dependence of reduced intrinsic magnetization on applied field for $J = 1/2$.

That is, when $T = T_\mathrm{C}$

$$\gamma_\mathrm{m} = 3kT_\mathrm{C}/[J(J+1)g^2\mu_\mathrm{B}^2 N_\mathrm{s}]$$

As an example, for metallic gadolinium,

$$T_\mathrm{C} = 293\ \mathrm{K}; \quad J = 7/2; \quad g = 2; \quad \text{to be} \quad \text{atomic weight M} = 157\cdot3$$

Also,

$$N = 6\cdot022 \times 10^{23}\ \mathrm{mole}^{-1}; \quad \mu_\mathrm{B} = 9\cdot274 \times 10^{-24}\ \mathrm{J\,T}^{-1};$$
$$k = 1\cdot381 \times 10^{-23}\ \mathrm{J\,K}^{-1}$$

Thus

$$\gamma_\mathrm{m} \approx 0\cdot6\ \mathrm{J}^{-1}\,\mathrm{T}^2\,\mathrm{kg}$$

The saturation magnetization of metallic Gd is

$$\sigma_{0,0} = 268\ \mathrm{J\,T}^{-1}\,\mathrm{kg}^{-1}$$

The molecular field at $T = 0$ is therefore expected to be

$$\gamma_\mathrm{m}\sigma_{0,0} = 157\ \mathrm{T}\ (= 1\cdot57 \times 10^6\ \mathrm{Oe})$$

γ_m may also be estimated in other ways. Relatively small differences occur between the different estimates, mostly because of deficiencies in the model used.

2.6.3 Susceptibility above the Curie temperature

At temperatures above the Curie temperature the magnetization is small and the molecular field is of the same order as the applied field. Again we may write

$$F(J, y') = \langle \mu_{J\uparrow} \rangle / Jg\mu_B = (J+1)y'/3J$$

Also,

$$y' = Jg\mu_B(B_0 + N_s\gamma_m\langle \mu_{J\uparrow}\rangle)/kT$$

Thus

$$N_s\langle \mu_{J\uparrow}\rangle = N_sJ(J+1)g^2\mu_B^2(B_0 + N_s\gamma_m\langle \mu_{J\uparrow}\rangle)/3kT$$

The susceptibility χ is the gross moment divided by the field. That is,

$$\chi = N_s\langle \mu_{J\uparrow}\rangle / B_0 = C/(T - \theta_p) \tag{2.11}$$

where

$$C = N_sp_{\text{eff}}^2/3k; \; \theta_p = N_s\gamma_mp_{\text{eff}}^2/3k \text{ and } p_{\text{eff}}^2 = g^2\mu_B^2J(J+1)$$

This is the Curie-Weiss law.

θ_p is identical in this treatment to the quantity T_C derived already. Experimentally, θ_p is usually slightly greater than T_C.

If the molar susceptibility is calculated instead,

$$\chi_m = C_M/(T - \theta_p)$$

where

$$C_M = Np_{\text{eff}}^2/3k$$

This value C_M is the same as the one calculated previously for non-interacting ions.

2.6.4 Comparison with experiment

The only rare earth metal that is a simple ferromagnet is gadolinium. The ionic (localized moment) model described here fits its basic magnetic properties quite well. The measured saturation magnetization is equivalent to a moment of $7\cdot55\,\mu_B$ per atom. This compares with the value $7\cdot0\,\mu_B$ expected for the 4f moment of a state $^8S_{7/2}$. The difference is thought to be due to an additional polarization of electrons more closely associated with conduction and related to the outermost atomic energy levels. The shape of the curve of intrinsic magnetization against temperature is reasonably close to that calculated for $J = S = 7/2$ (Fig. 2.13).

The susceptibility above the Curie temperature follows the Curie-Weiss law well, and the experimental value for p_{eff} is $7\cdot98$ compared with the theoretical value of $7\cdot94$ for the $^8S_{7/2}$ state. It is notable that the excess moment attributed to outer electrons does not appear to occur in the paramagnetic state.

For ferromagnetic transition metals and also their alloys the agreement

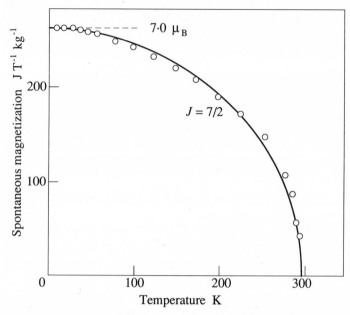

Figure 2.13 Spontaneous magnetization of single-crystal gadolinium, measured along the b-axis in the basal plane.

is less satisfactory. Above the Curie temperature the susceptibility often follows a Curie-Weiss law approximately. But there are many examples of graphs of χ^{-1} against T that are curved. Measured values of p_{eff} do not correlate with the ionic theory or with the saturation magnetization. The moment per atom derived from the saturation magnetization is usually a non-integral multiple of the Bohr magneton. This is inconsistent with the ionic theory presented here.

Chapter 3 _____

Magnetism associated with band electrons

In Chapter 2 we considered the magnetism of electrons that may be treated as though they were contained within the cores of atoms in solids. The essential interactions which we expressed as a molecular field are between atoms and the requirement for a paramagnetic or ferromagnetic state was the existence of incompletely filled inner shells of electrons. The paramagnetic susceptibility found in these circumstances varies markedly with temperature, ideally following the Curie Law or the Curie-Weiss Law.

In describing most properties of metals we often need to adopt a different approach, in which possible energy states relate to electrons treated collectively as waves travelling through the whole crystalline solid. In metals, magnetism must be considered to some extent as a collective phenomenon. Many metallic elements are only weakly paramagnetic and their susceptibility varies little or not at all with temperature (see Fig. 3.1). Examples are the alkali metals Li, Na, K, Rb and Cs, the properties of which cannot be explained on the localized model. The explanation is based on the paramagnetism of a gas of electrons free to move throughout space occupied by the metal. The electrons also provide a bonding mechanism for the metal as a whole.

The first approximation in the collective electron treatment is that of free electrons constrained only by the potential box formed by the external dimensions of the whole specimen. Since the size of the box is large compared with atomic dimensions the available energy levels of the electrons are very closely spaced and are effectively continuous. The energy is purely kinetic and the number of electron states per unit energy range is proportional to the square root of the energy. The effect of the periodic field of the crystal lattice is to modify the distribution of states, giving rise to a series of energy bands, separate or overlapping. In general, near the bottom of a band the energy density of states depends on the energy in the same way as for free electrons, though with a different proportionality factor. This also holds for hole states near the top of a band, the energy being measured downwards from the upper limit.

The salient characteristics of metals depend on the electrons in unfilled bands. In particular, the ferromagnetism of iron, nickel and cobalt derives

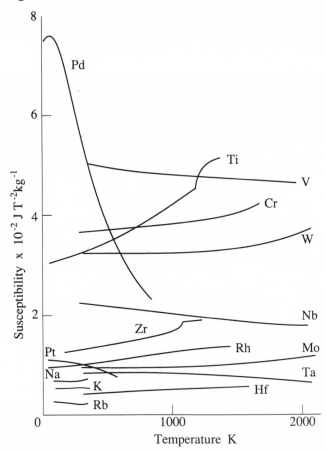

Figure 3.1 Temperature dependence of the magnetic susceptibility of several metals (after Kittel, *Introduction to Solid State Physics*, Wiley).

from electrons in the partially filled band corresponding to the d-states in the free atoms. The exchange interaction is such that, at the lowest temperatures, instead of the electrons occupying the lowest states in balanced pairs, there is an excess of electrons with spins pointing in one direction only, thus giving rise to a spontaneous magnetization. The equilibrium magnetization depends on the number of electrons, the magnitude of the exchange interaction and the temperature. It must be calculated on the basis of Fermi-Dirac statistics. Surprisingly the form of the band has little influence.

3.1 Collective electron theory: general solution

Stoner first published this collective electron theory. He simplified the treatment by converting the more usual dimensioned quantities to equivalent dimensionless quantities, as follows.

The parameters E_0, θ', θ and ζ are used. ε_0 is the maximum particle energy at the absolute zero. Where this refers to holes in a nearly full band (Fig. 3.2) this is reckoned downards from the top of the band. $k\theta'$ (where k is the Boltzmann constant) is a measure of the interaction energy. θ is the Curie temperature. ζ is the relative magnetization, which is the ratio of the number of excess parallel spins to the total number of potentially effective spins at full saturation. ζ_0 is the value of ζ at zero temperature. In the classical limit $\zeta_0 = 1$ and also $\theta' = \theta$. What the theory seeks to do is to establish ζ as a function of the temperature T for a variety of conditions, in particular for different values of the interaction parameter. Above the Curie temperature, where $T > \theta$, the output of the theory is the dependence of the susceptibility on temperature.

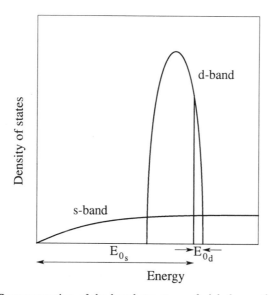

Figure 3.2 Representation of the band structure of nickel near the Fermi level.

A simple quantum mechanical treatment shows that the density of electron state $\nu(\varepsilon)$ varies parabolically with the energy ε.

$$\nu(\varepsilon) = (dz/d\varepsilon) = a\varepsilon^{1/2} \tag{3.1}$$

where a is a constant and z is the number of electron states with energy ε.

This is the number of states, which on average may be filled with up to two electrons (or holes) per state, one of each direction of spin. At $T = 0$ and when no field is applied there are two per state at all energies up to the limiting Fermi energy, no electrons having higher energies.

The number of electrons per state (both spin directions) is given by $2f = 2[\exp\{(\varepsilon - \eta)/kT\} + 1]^{-1}$. η is a numerical factor equal to the limiting energy ε_0 at $T = 0$. At room temperature kT/ε_0 is of the order of 10^{-2} and at all temperatures encountered in dealing with the metallic state η differs very little from ε_0. The variation of f with ε is shown in Figure 3.3. The

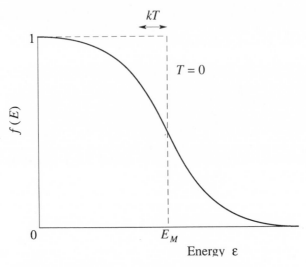

Figure 3.3 Fermi-Dirac function plotted against energy.

energy of an electron is made up of a non-magnetic part ε and a magnetic part ε', which may be written

$$\varepsilon' = \varepsilon_1 + \varepsilon_2$$

ε_1 is provided by the interactions and ε_2 derives from applying an external magnetic field. For the interactions we write

$$\varepsilon_1 = \pm k\theta' \zeta$$

$k\theta'$, being a measure of the exchange interaction energy, is such that $2k\theta'\zeta$ is the difference in energy for the spin parallel and antiparallel to the magnetization. The difference in energy per electron between the completely magnetized state ($\zeta = 1$) and the demagnetized state is $1/2k\theta'$. When an external magnetic field is applied this energy is enhanced by an amount $\varepsilon_2 = \mu_B B_0$, so that $\varepsilon' = \pm (k\theta'\zeta + \mu_B B_0)$. The parts $k\theta'\zeta$ and $\mu_B B_0$ always act in the same direction.

Pauli spin paramagnetism then becomes a special, non-interacting, case of this situation, for which $k\theta' = 0$. We will examine this case shortly.

The total number of electrons N in the band must be equal to the sum of the numbers N^+ and N^- having the two spin directions, while the magnetization is the difference $(N^+ - N^-)$ times the moment μ_B of one electron.

For the up-spin number N^+ we write

$$N^+ = \int_0^\infty (\mathrm{d}z/\mathrm{d}\varepsilon) f(\varepsilon - \varepsilon')\mathrm{d}\varepsilon$$

$$= \int_0^\infty (\mathrm{d}z/\mathrm{d}\varepsilon)[\exp\{(\varepsilon - \varepsilon' - \eta)/kT\} + 1]^{-1}\mathrm{d}\varepsilon \qquad (3.2)$$

We use the following abbreviations

$$\eta' = \eta/kT$$

$$\beta = k\theta'\zeta/kT$$

$$\beta' = \mu_B B_0/kT$$

$$(\beta + \beta') = \varepsilon'/kT$$

$x = \varepsilon/kT$, so that $\varepsilon^{1/2}d\varepsilon = (kT)^{3/2}x^{1/2}dx$ and

$(dz/d\varepsilon)d\varepsilon = a\varepsilon^{1/2}(d\varepsilon)$ becomes $(dz/d\varepsilon)d\varepsilon = a(kT)^{3/2}x^{1/2}dx$

a actually has the value $3/4N/\varepsilon_0^{3/2}$, where N is the total number of electrons in the band.

Thus $N^+ = 3/4N(kT/\varepsilon_0)^{3/2}F_{1/2}(\eta' + \beta + \beta')$ \hfill (3.3)

and similarly

$$N^- = 3/4N(kT/\varepsilon_0)^{3/2}F_{1/2}(\eta' - \beta - \beta') \tag{3.4}$$

The integral

$$F_{1/2}(\rho) = \int x^{1/2}[\exp\{x - \rho\} + 1]^{-1}\,dx$$

is one of a set of Fermi-Dirac integrals, the values of which have been determined numerically and are available in tabulated form.

The total number of electrons in the band $N = N^+ + N^-$ becomes

$$N = 3/4N(kT/\varepsilon_0)^{3/2}[F_{1/2}(\eta' + \beta + \beta') + F_{1/2}(\eta' - \beta - \beta')] \tag{3.5}$$

This equation serves to fix the parameter η' (and hence η).

The magnetization per unit volume $M = (N^+ - N^-)\mu_B$ becomes

$$M = 3/4N\mu_B(kT/\varepsilon_0)^{3/2}[F_{1/2}(\eta' + \beta + \beta') - F_{1/2}(\eta' - \beta - \beta')] \tag{3.6}$$

The solution of these two equations for the various conditions appropriate to the model is all that is in the basic theory. The most important cases are given below.

It is convenient to deal with the relative magnetization ζ.

$$\zeta = \frac{M}{N\mu_B} = \frac{F_{1/2}(\eta' + \beta + \beta') - F_{1/2}(\eta' - \beta - \beta')}{F_{1/2}(\eta' + \beta + \beta') + F_{1/2}(\eta' - \beta - \beta')} = F'/F \tag{3.7}$$

3.2 Paramagnetism without interactions

In this case $k\theta'/\varepsilon_0 = 0$ and $B = 0$. The magnetization M is given by

$$M = 3/4N\mu_B(kT/\varepsilon_0)^{3/2}[F_{1/2}(\eta' + \beta') - F_{1/2}(\eta' - \beta')]$$

where β' is very small compared with η'.

The relative magnetization ζ is

$$\zeta = F'/F, \text{ where } F' = [F_{1/2}(\eta' + \beta') - F_{1/2}(\eta' - \beta')] \tag{3.8}$$

$$\text{and } F = [F_{1/2}(\eta' + \beta') + F_{1/2}(\eta' - \beta')]$$

Even in very strong fields $B_0\mu_B/\varepsilon_0$ will only be of the order of 10^{-3}, and the magnetization becomes

$$M = 2\mu_B^2 B_0 \nu(\varepsilon_0)$$

The susceptibility per unit volume at $T = 0$ is then

$$\kappa_0 = M/B_0 = 2\mu_B^2 \nu(\varepsilon_0) \tag{3.9}$$

The cases where this model usually applies are those for which there are relatively few magnetically effective electrons in a conduction band and we deal with electrons rather than holes. Then ε_0 is a large energy, of the order of the Fermi energy E_m and thus the susceptibility is a measure of the density of electron states at the Fermi level.

In this case, when the temperature is so high that kT is not entirely insignificant, the volume susceptibility κ is approximately equal to

$$\kappa = \kappa_0[1 - (\pi^2/12)(kT/E_m)^2 + \ldots] \tag{3.10}$$

Since kT is here always very much less than E_m this is a very small decrease with increasing temperature. The susceptibility of a free electron gas is essentially independent of temperature. In Figure 3.4 the calculated inverse susceptibility is reduced to an equivalent dimensionless quantity $(\mu B_0)/(\zeta\varepsilon_0)$ and plotted against a reduced temperature parameter (kT/ε_0). Only a small range of (kT/ε_0) on this graph is accessible within the solid state.

3.2.1 Comparison with experiment

In actual metals the free electron model does not hold exactly and the density of states differs from a simple parabolic form. In the least complicated case of the alkali metals the deviation can be taken into account by replacing the electronic mass m by the effective mass m^*.

Before the results of the theory can be compared with experiment various other more complicated effects must be allowed for. Electron–electron interaction (exchange and correlation) is not entirely absent, although for heavier elements the effect is not known very accurately. Correction for diamagnetism is also necessary. The diamagnetic effect of the ion core increases considerably as the atomic number increases although it remains relatively small. There is another effect called the Landau diamagnetism. It describes the orientation of the quantized orbital angular momenta in the external magnetic field. For free electrons its absolute magnitude is one third of the paramagnetic susceptibility due to spin, but it is influenced considerably by changes in effective mass.

Table 3.1 shows the mass susceptibility of alkali metals. The first column (a) gives the experimental value of the total susceptibility. The second column (b) gives available values of the spin susceptibility, not subject to diamagnetic effects and derived from magnetic resonance experiments. The remaining columns give the theoretical estimates: (c) free electron paramagnetic susceptibility (Pauli); (d) susceptibility corrected for effective mass, exchange and correlation; and (e) corrected for diamagnetism.

Table 3.1 Experimental and calculated mass susceptibilities of alkali metals

	Experiment		Theory		
	(a) χ_{total}	(b) χ_{spin}	(c) χ_p	(d) $\chi_p^{(corr)}$	(e) χ_{total}
Li	3·60	3·83	1·44	4·00	3·60
Na	0·61	1·12	0·65	0·85	0·42
K	0·46	—	0·59	0·81	0·24
Rb	0·20	—	0·30	0·49	0·11
Cs	0·26	—	0·23	0·57	0·23

The agreement respectively between columns (b) and (d); and between (a) and (e) is quite good.

For other metals that are less simple than the alkalis the theory is more difficult. The effective masses in such metals are anisotropic and often show large variations. The band shape is usually far from the simple parabolic form. And in many cases the effect of exchange is strong. Most transition metals, with unfilled inner electron shells represented by bands of relatively high density states, are much more strongly paramagnetic than the alkali metals, and their susceptibility usually depends significantly on temperature.

3.3 Paramagnetism with interactions

The magnetization here is still weak and proportional to the external field. The interaction parameter $(k\theta'/\varepsilon_0)$ is small but not zero. β and β' are of similar order, small and finite.

The results of the calculation are shown in Figure 3.4. The effect is to displace the reduced inverse susceptibility downwards by a constant amount which is the interaction parameter $(k\theta'/\varepsilon_0)$. That is to say, the susceptibility is enhanced by the effect of interactions.

3.3.1 Comparison with experiment

This so-called Stoner enhancement of the susceptibility occurs in some transition metals such as palladium and platinum. The interactions are strong enough to cause enhancement but not strong enough to establish magnetic order (ferromagnetism or antiferromagnetism). Such materials can readily be triggered into a quasi-ferromagnetic state in alloys and intermetallic compounds. For example, a small amount of iron dissolved in palladium induces an appreciable magnetic moment on the palladium.

3.4 Ferromagnetism in the band model

If the form of Figure 3.4 is considered, the question arises as to what happens when the interaction parameter $(k\theta'/\varepsilon_0)$ is so great that the

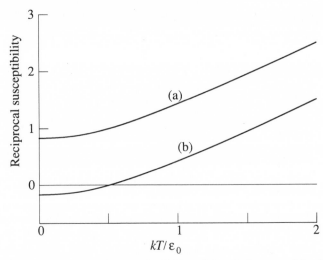

Figure 3.4 Calculated reciprocal susceptibility of band electrons (a) without and (b) with interaction (after Stoner, 1951, *J. Physique*, **12**, 377).

equivalent of line (b) meets the horizontal axis. Here is where a spontaneous ferromagnetic state is generated. When there is no external field the equation for the reduced magnetization ζ becomes

$$\zeta = F'/F, \text{ with } F' = [F(\eta' + \beta) - F(\eta' - \beta)] \text{ and} \qquad (3.11)$$

$$F = [F(\eta' + \beta) + F(\eta' - \beta)]$$

β is proportional to the magnetization, as we have seen already, and is not necessarily small.

The solutions for ζ as a function of (kT/ε_0) are shown in Figure 3.5, for varying values of the interaction parameter $(k\theta'/\varepsilon_0)$. We note that for relatively weaker interactions the value of ζ at zero temperature $(= \zeta_0)$ is less than the saturation value, as shown in Figure 3.6. The critical value of the interaction parameter $(k\theta'/\varepsilon_0)$, below which there is no ferromagnetism at all is $2/3 = 0.6667$. It must reach a value of $2^{-1/3} = 0.7937$ for there to be fully saturated ferromagnetism.

We call the state weak itinerant ferromagnetism when saturation is not reached, for $0.6667 < (k\theta'/\varepsilon_0) < 0.7937$. Otherwise we have strong itinerant ferromagnetism. One of the ways of distinguishing these two states is that in the weak case the magnetization varies strongly with applied field, even at very low temperatures.

The intermetallic compound $ZrZn_2$ is ferromagnetic, in spite of containing no magnetic elements. It is thought to be a weak itinerant ferromagnet, in which the magnetic moment is diffused widely through the crystal lattice. Its properties are shown in Figure 3.7.

When $k\theta'/\varepsilon_0$ lies between $2/3 = 0.6667$ and $2^{-1/3} = 0.7937$ the reduced magnetization at $T = 0$ $(= \zeta_0)$ is less than unity (Fig. 3.6).

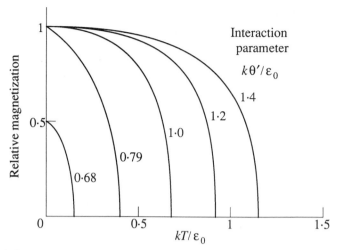

Figure 3.5 Dependence on temperature of the calculated reduced magnetization of band electrons for various strengths of the interaction parameter.

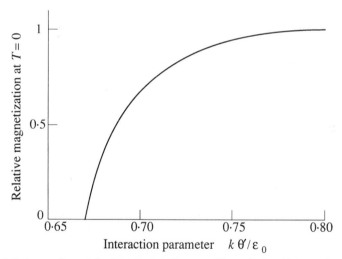

Figure 3.6 Saturation of the ferromagnetic state. The calculated dependence of the relative magnetization at zero temperature on the value of the interaction parameter.

3.4.1 Paramagnetism above the Curie temperature

Figure 3.8 shows how the calculated reduced inverse susceptibility above the Curie temperature depends on temperature for various strengths of interaction. The $(1/\chi, T)$ relationship sometimes shows curvature, so

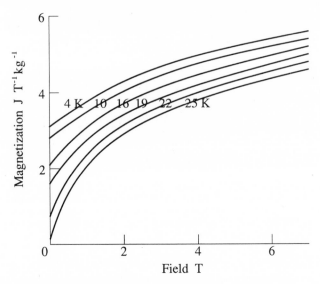

Figure 3.7 Experimental dependence of the intrinsic magnetization of $ZrZn_2$ at temperatures near and below the Curie temperature.

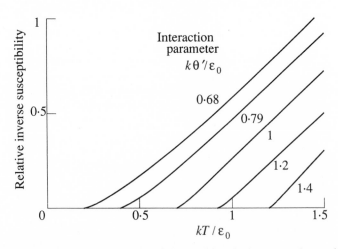

Figure 3.8 Calculated inverse susceptibility of band electrons above the Curie temperature for various strengths of the interaction parameter.

deviating from a Curie-Weiss law. This is found experimentally in some alloys, although the effect is a weak one.

Under experimental conditions it would not be obvious when a value of the reduced magnetization ζ_0 at $T = 0$ was less than unity. For purposes of comparison between theory and experiment, therefore, it is useful to calculate values of ζ/ζ_0 and to plot them against T/T_C (Fig. 3.9). These

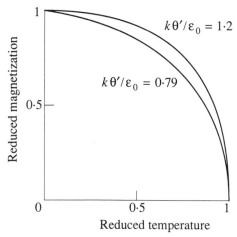

Figure 3.9 Calculated curves of reduced magnetization against reduced temperature for band electrons, with two different values of the interaction parameter.

curves agree fairly well with what is found experimentally in several alloy
systems, for instance solid solutions of nickel containing increasing
amounts of copper in solution (Fig. 3.10).

This model forms the basis of an understanding of the magnetic
properties of metals in which the electrons that are the source of the
magnetism are in energy bands of finite width. Considering how simple the
model is the extent of the fit with experiment is good. It agrees with the
experimental result that ferromagnetic moments are not necessarily integral multiples of the Bohr magneton, and explains plausibly how the
magnetic properties of solid solution alloys can vary smoothly with alloy
composition. The model behaves quite well in predicting the detail of not
only magnetizations and susceptibilities but also the thermal characteristics
associated with the magnetism, but is too simple to explain some of the
other effects (such as spin wave properties) that are observed experimentally.

3.5 Magnetic moments of pure metals and alloys

The collective electron model is most applicable to metals in which there is
band overlap between electron energy bands, one of which is wide in
energy and not very deep in density of states (relatively free electrons); and
the other of which is narrow in energy and with a relatively high density of
states. How this arises is shown in Figure 3.11, which refers to copper. The
Fermi energy is above the highest 3d level and there are no vacancies in the
3d band.

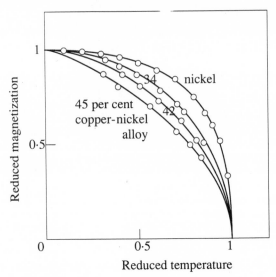

Figure 3.10 Experimental curves of reduced magnetization against reduced temperature for a series of nickel–copper alloys.

3.5.1 The rigid band model

What follows depends on the applicability of the so-called rigid band model. This assumes that when two (similar) elements that are not too far apart in the periodic table are alloyed together substitutionally in solid solution, their atoms contribute jointly to a common band structure. The Fermi level is then supposed to be determined by the concentration and effective valencies of the constituent elements, and their effect on the overall electron/atom ratio. The model is not very strongly supported theoretically although it has a fair experimental justification. It must be used with caution, but is useful in leading to a first-order understanding of many experimental observations. The model makes possible the continuous alteration of the electron content of an incomplete energy band. For instance, taking copper (eleven 3d + 4s electrons) and alloying it with an increasing proportion of nickel (with the next lower atomic number and ten 3d + 4s electrons) it is expected that the Fermi level will fall until eventually vacancies occur in the 3d band. It is known from experiment that the boundary between ferromagnetism and no ferromagnetism at $T = 0$ is at an alloy composition of about 53 atomic per cent of copper and 47 atomic per cent of nickel.

3.5.2 Nickel

The value for the saturation magnetization of pure nickel at $T = 0$ is $\sigma_{0,0} = 58 \cdot 6 \, \text{J T}^{-1} \, \text{kg}^{-1}$. This value is about $1 \cdot 6$ per cent higher than the one measured by Weiss and Forrer (1926) and for long accepted as a standard.

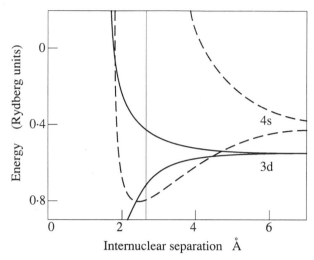

Figure 3.11 Energy bands of copper as a function of internuclear separation. The equilibrium distance between nuclei is indicated by the thin vertical line (after Krutter, 1935, *Phys. Rev.*, **48**, 664).

Thus in accepting old data on saturation magnetization it is necessary to find out what standard was used and if appropriate to apply a correction. The saturation magnetization of nickel is equivalent to a Bohr magneton number $p = gJ = 0.616$. The best value for g is 2.185. Thus the number of uncompensated spins per atom is 0.563. If the magnetic electrons are 3d electrons and the 3d band contains its full quota (five per atom) of electrons with positive spin, all the vacancies giving rise to the magnetic moment will be on the negative side. Since in nickel the total of 3d + 4s electrons is ten, there must be 0.56 4s electrons per atom in the metal. This number is slightly lower than the number of conduction electrons obtained from observations on the Hall effect suggesting that 3d electrons might contribute to conduction in nickel to a small degree, as well as 4s electrons.

3.5.3 Cobalt

In pure cobalt a change of phase occurs near 400 °C, the equilibrium crystal structure being face-centred cubic at temperatures above the change and close-packed hexagonal below. Both phases are ferromagnetic with high Curie temperatures, that of the cubic phase being above 1100 °C. The hexagonal phase is strongly anistropic magnetically. Its saturation magnetization, measured on single crystals oriented along their magnetic easy direction, is equivalent to a magneton number of $1.715 \, \mu_B$. That of the cubic phase (extrapolated from measurements carried out at temperatures above the phase transformation) is $1.751 \, \mu_B$. The g value is 2.170. Applying this g value to both phases gives differences in the number of positive and negative spins per atom of 1.61 and 1.58 for the cubic and hexagonal phases, respectively. The total number of 3d + 4s electrons in cobalt is nine. There is no direct evidence to show the exact distribution of the electrons, but the changes in magnetic properties on alloying seem to point to the 3d positive sub-band having its full quota of five electrons, with about 1·6 vacancies per atom on the negative side.

3.5.4 Iron

The magneton number of body-centred cubic iron is 2·22 μ_B. The g-value is 2·094. Thus the difference between the numbers of positive and negative spins per atom is 2·12.

Again there is no direct evidence on the distribution of the outer electrons. However, the total number of 3d + 4s electrons in iron is eight, and if all the 3d vacancies were of the same sign there would only be 0·12 4s conduction electrons per atom. This seems to be rather too small in comparison to the equivalent number for Cu, Ni and Co. In addition, alloying behaviour suggests that vacancies of both signs occur in the 3d band, with roughly one electron per atom in the s-band.

Face-centred cubic pure iron is not stable below about 900 °C, but when it is stabilized by the addition of various alloying elements it is non-ferromagnetic even at very low temperatures. It has been shown that an austenitic (face-centred cubic) steel containing 18·6 per cent of Cr and 9 per cent of Ni has a paramagnetic susceptibility which behaves in a way characteristic of an antiferromagnetic material below 40 K, and it has been inferred that if pure face-centred cubic iron existed at low enough temperatures, it would be antiferromagnetic.

At very high pressures iron has a close packed hexagonal structure. Nothing is yet known about the magnetic properties of this phase.

Schematic density of states curves for nickel, cobalt and iron are shown in Figure 3.12. The split in energy between 3d positive and negative sub-bands indicates the size of the exchange interaction, as measured by T_C.

3.5.5 Face-centred cubic nickel–copper and cobalt–copper alloys

Copper dissolves in nickel continuously over the whole range of composition, with no change of crystal structure. The saturation magnetization (and therefore the magneton number) varies linearly with composition and extrapolates to $p = 0$ at 53 atomic per cent of copper, where the mean number of 3d + 4s electrons is 10·53. The g-value of nickel–copper alloys is substantially independent of composition and equal to the value for pure nickel. The average number of uncompensated spins per atom of the alloy thus varies linearly with composition, from 631 K for pure nickel to zero at the composition where the magneton number falls to zero.

The experimental behaviour is therefore in broad agreement with the simple rigid band model. One difficulty is that copper-rich nickel–copper alloys are strongly paramagnetic in spite of the vacant holes in the 3d band

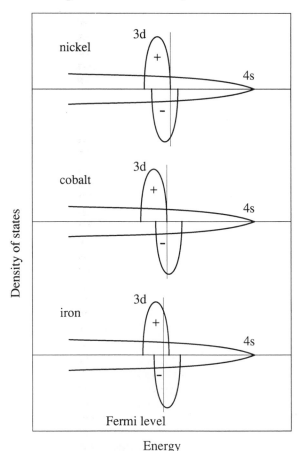

Figure 3.12 Schematic density of states graphs for nickel, cobalt and iron. The energy splitting between + and − directions is a measure of the exchange energy.

having apparently been filled. This is because the model is too simple and there is not an absolutely uniform magnetic state on an atomic scale throughout the metal. There are other difficulties of detail when an exact comparison between experiment and the basic collective electron model is made.

In the case of cobalt–copper alloys there are experimental difficulties in that the solubility of cobalt in copper is only about 9 atomic per cent and also the phase constitution is less simple. However, the rate of change of magneton number with composition has been measured. It is equivalent to a variation of the number of uncompensated spins per atom with total number of 3d + 4s electrons per atom of 1.04 spins per electron. This number coincides with the equivalent quantity for nickel–copper alloys, again agreeing with the rigid band model.

3.5.6 Other alloys of nickel and cobalt

Several elements in the central groups of the periodic table form substitutional alloys with nickel and cobalt, and it is generally supposed that they can act as donors of electrons to the structure. If it is assumed that the loosely bound electrons (valence electrons) outside the inner closed shells in the atoms of the solute elements are available for transfer to the vacant states in the 3d band of the solvent, correlation is expected between the rate of change of magneton number p with composition c and the normal valency q of the solute. Such agreement is found experimentally. Higher solute valency corresponds to a faster rate of decrease dp/dc of the magneton number. The quantity $(1/q)dp/dc$ is approximately constant for a number of binary alloys of nickel, as is shown in Table 3.2.

Table 3.2 Dependence of rate of dilution of magnetic moment dp/dc on the valency q of the solute element in binary nickel alloys

Solute element	Valency	dp/dc	$(1/q)dp/dc$
Cu	1	1·14	1·14
Zn	2	2·11	1·06
Al	3	2·80	0·93
Si	4	3·77	0·94
Ge	4	3·70	0·93
Sn	4	4·22	1·06
Sb	5	5·31	1·06

A limited number of alloys based on face-centred cubic cobalt show broadly similar behaviour, but the numerical correlation is much poorer.

Relatively few non-transition elements form extensive solid solutions based on iron in the body-centred cubic phase. Those that do form solutions simply act magnetically as diluents and leave the magnetic moment per iron atom unchanged. Elements that act in this way are aluminium, silicon and tin.

There is no evidence to distinguish between whether the solute supplies electrons in equal numbers to offset vacancies in the 3d band of iron which are probably present for electrons with either spin, or whether the solute supplies no electrons at all to the iron 3d band.

3.5.7 Face-centred cubic binary alloys between transition elements

Wide ranges of solid solution exist in many of the alloys between elements of the first transition series. In Figure 3.13 the mean number of uncompensated spins per atom, derived from the experimental values of magneton numbers and g factors, is plotted against the average number of 3d + 4s electrons per atom, for several such alloy systems. The data for nickel–copper and cobalt–copper alloys are included in the diagram.

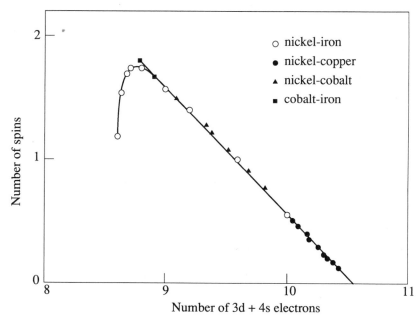

Figure 3.13 Number of magnetic electron spins per atom plotted against the average number of (3d + 4s) electrons per atom for face-centred cubic binary alloys.

The outstanding feature of this graph is that over wide ranges of composition the data for many systems lie exactly on the straight line drawn between the points for pure nickel and for pure cobalt. These systems include nickel–copper, nickel–iron, nickel–cobalt, cobalt–copper and cobalt–iron.

Deviations from the common line (not shown here) occur whenever the solute has a lower atomic number than that of iron and also when the solute is iron in high concentration.

The occurrence of this common straight line having a slope near to unity is regarded as supporting the application of the rigid band model to those systems which lie on it. The picture is of a common 3d band shared by both elements present, the Fermi level varying as the average electron density changes with varying composition. Such a description would seem to apply at the top of the 3d band and for elements of atomic number not less than that of iron. It could be seen as a consequence of the spatial overlap between the 3d-like charge distributions of neighbouring atoms being strongest where the ion cores are largest.

Where deviations from the common line occur it would seem that the smaller ions are reacting individually. Since they do not appear to act as simple diluents to the magnetization of the solvent, they seem therefore to possess magnetic moments of their own, which are at least partially aligned by interaction with the solvent atoms. The existence of localized characteristic magnetic moments on solute atoms has been confirmed in a few of these cases by neutron diffraction.

In some of those alloys in which deviations from the common line occur most rapidly the existence of an antiferromagnetic state at higher solute contents has been either confirmed or is suspected. For instance, antiferromagnetism occurs in the nickel–manganese system and is suspected in the face-centred cubic phase of the nickel–iron system at high iron concentrations. It may be that the steepness of the line is somehow related to the onset of an antiferromagnetic state.

When body-centred cubic alloys are similarly examined, Figure 3.14 is obtained. In this crystal structure, no overlap occurs between data for different alloy systems even for solutes in iron which are neighbouring elements. Here there seems to be no question of both kinds of atom in a binary alloy contributing to a common 3d band. Their magnetic moments seem always to act individually.

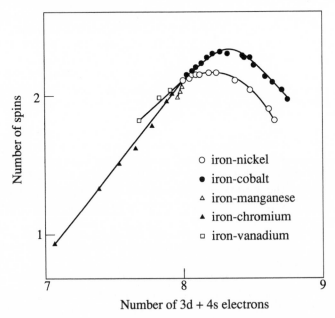

○ iron-nickel
● iron-cobalt
△ iron-manganese
▲ iron-chromium
□ iron-vanadium

Figure 3.14 Number of magnetic electron spins per atom plotted against the average number of (3d + 4s) electrons per atom for body-centred cubic binary alloys.

Chapter 4 _____

Techniques of making magnetic measurements

Since magnetism is such a wide-ranging subject, there is a vast range of techniques that are used to measure all the different magnetic parameters that are of interest. In this book we can only sample them selectively, trying to give an insight into the main methods used. The choice of topics is necessarily arbitrary and there is no reason to suppose that these are the only or the best methods. The only justification is that they are widely used, or that the author has experience of using them and therefore understands them better than other techniques and is more able to write about their merits or demerits.

This chapter is first divided into the acquisition of experimental information leading to understanding intrinsic or fundamental properties; then into measuring quantities important in technical magnetism; and then into describing and evaluating the fundamentals of experimentation (such as the generation of magnetic fields) that are important in all the areas discussed.

4.1 Measurement of magnetization

The magnetization of ferromagnetic specimens may be measured in three main ways: the induction method, the force method, and methods based on the detection of the dipole field of a magnetized specimen. The methods are the same whether the aim is to get intrinsic or technical information.

4.1.1 The induction method (also called the extraction method)

If a magnetic dipole initially placed at the centre of a coil is removed to a large distance a voltage e is induced in the coil, the time integral $\int e \, dt$ of which is equal to the flux ϕ produced by the dipole. The pick-up coils can be located inside a solenoid or other source of field so that the moment can be measured as a function of externally applied field.

The total flux ϕ is given by $\phi = \int B \, dS$ over the sample, where dS is an element of area. The induction B is given by

$$B = B_0 + \mu_0 M$$

If the applied field B_0 is known sufficiently accurately or if it can be compensated out, the magnetization is given directly from ϕ.

Ideally the measured flux change should be from the experimental sample alone and changes in the magnetizing field should not contribute. Unfortunately it is impossible to design a practical coil system that is ideal. A secondary pick-up coil is connected in series opposition to the first, positioned so that it senses changes in the magnetizing field but not in the effect of the dipole. By adjusting the relative contributions of the pick-up coils, fairly good compensation can be achieved. The design of good pick-up coils is complicated.

An experimental arrangement using this method is shown schematically in Figure 4.1. The specimen is withdrawn mechanically from the coil system and the flux change is measured by means of an integrating device which is usually electronic (Section 4.6.4).

One of the difficulties with this method is that it is prone to errors due to magnetic images. When a magnetic pole is placed near the surface of a ferromagnetic body local magnetic pole density is generated and the effect is as though an image is produced at an equivalent position inside the surface, just as an image would be produced in a mirror with light. When the source is a dipole the image is a dipole which interacts with the real dipole. In particular, the image when present causes errors in measurements of dipole moment. The strength of the image depends on the

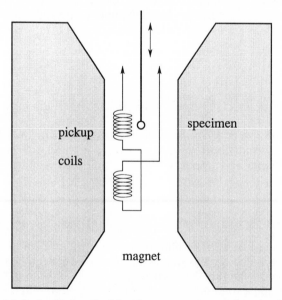

Figure 4.1 Induction method for the measurement of magnetization.

permeability of the ferromagnetic surface which produces it and it is difficult to evaluate accurately. If the surface is the pole face of a magnet its permeability varies with the state of saturation of the face, thus producing indeterminate errors in measurements of dipole moment which vary with applied field. The errors are particularly troublesome in induction measurements of magnetization and great care is necessary to eliminate them.

Exactly similar images are produced when the surface is a superconductor, for example in a superconducting solenoid, although in this case the sign of the image is reversed.

This image effect is probably the greatest drawback in the use of the extraction method.

4.1.2 Vibrating sample magnetometer

Another form of the induction method which is convenient and popular is the vibrating sample magnetometer (VSM). The sample dipole is subjected to mechanical vibration, generating an alternating signal in a coil placed round it.

In the form shown in Figure 4.2 the specimen is vibrated at right angles to the magnetizing field at a fixed frequency of about 80 Hz and the alternating inductive signal generated in the surrounding pick-up coils is an alternating one. The pick-up coils are placed with their axes perpendicular to the main magnetizing field, so as to minimize error signals arising from field fluctuations. In any case, a sharply tuned signal-detecting system reduces unwanted background signals to a very low level. However, the transmission of spurious vibrations at the measured frequency must be carefully avoided, and this is usually done by attaching a small permanent

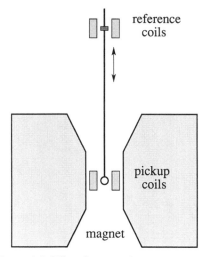

Figure 4.2 Vibrating sample magnetometer.

magnet to a remote part of the vibrating system. This moves inside its own pick-up coils and provides a reference signal against which the signal produced by the sample can be measured accurately.

This method of measuring magnetization is a relatively sensitive one and it is claimed to be insensitive to images because of the right-angle geometry. Good sensitivity and low errors due to unwanted noise signals are obtained by using modern lock-in amplifiers with phase-sensitive detection for measuring the coil output and comparing it with the signal from the reference coil. In the latest developments, methods based on the digital signal handling developed in the communications industry are used.

4.1.3 The force method

The force acting on a magnetizable specimen situated in a (non-uniform) magnetic field may be calculated from the variation of its free energy with position. When the magnetization is uniform throughout the specimen and the field varies with position, the force is given by

$$F = -VM \cdot \nabla B_0 = -m\boldsymbol{\sigma} \cdot \nabla B_0 \qquad (4.1)$$

where V and m are the volume and the mass of the specimen respectively. Writing Equation (4.1) in its cartesian component form we have (neglecting the negative sign)

$$(1/m)|F_x| = \sigma_x \partial B_0^x/\partial x + \sigma_y \partial B_0^y/\partial x + \sigma_z \partial B_0^z/\partial x$$
$$(1/m)|F_y| = \sigma_x \partial B_0^x/\partial y + \sigma_y \partial B_0^y/\partial y + \sigma_z \partial B_0^z/\partial y \qquad (4.2)$$
$$(1/m)|F_z| = \sigma_x \partial B_0^x/\partial z + \sigma_y \partial B_0^y/\partial z + \sigma_z \partial B_0^z/\partial z$$

The directions of x, y and z are shown in Figure 4.3.

Various experimental arrangements simplify Equations (4.2) in different ways. Nearly all use long thin specimens (ideally prolate ellipsoids) aligned along the x direction (field direction). Thus $\sigma_x = \sigma$, $\sigma_y = 0$ and $\sigma_z = 0$. It is often possible to use a balance sensitive only in a single direction, and so to measure only one component of force. A commonly used method mea-

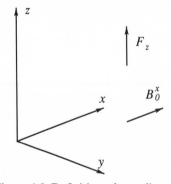

Figure 4.3 Definition of coordinates.

sures the vertical force F on a specimen situated in a field B_0^x having a vertical gradient dB_0^x/dz (Fig. 4.4).

A number of different force balances are used. One, which is an adaptation of a conventional automatic weighing balance, is illustrated in Figure 4.4. Different systems are used, having different sensitivities according to the range of forces it is required to measure. The main

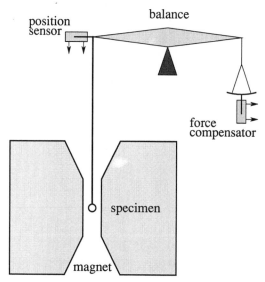

Figure 4.4 Force method for measuring magnetization.

problem is to prevent the specimen, which is often small (about 50 mg) from moving during the measurement to a position where the field gradient is different. Forces are typically up to 0·05 N (5000 dynes). Magnetic images do not usually affect this method much, because the principal images are usually formed at right angles to the direction of the measurement. What remains is only a small second-order correction.

Field gradients may be produced (Fig. 4.5) either by shaping the pole

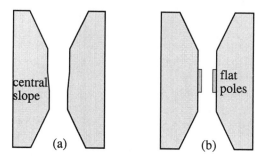

Figure 4.5 The production of field gradient: (a) with shaped poles; (b) with parallel conductors.

tips of the electromagnet or by superposing a field gradient produced by an electric current on the magnetizing field.

Nearly all magnetization measurements made by any method are made relative to a standard specimen. In the force method this avoids having to measure field gradients accurately. Suitable standard materials are pure iron or pure nickel and their magnetizations are given in Table 4.1.

Ideally any method should be capable of running automatically, under computer control, with automatic collection of the data on the computer.

Table 4.1 Magnetization and susceptibility standards

Material	Magnetization ($J\ T^{-1}\ kg^{-1}$)		
	293 K	77 K	4 K
nickel	$55\cdot1\pm0\cdot1$	$58\cdot4\pm0\cdot1$	$58\cdot6\pm0\cdot1$
iron	$217\cdot6\pm0\cdot1$	$221\cdot4\pm0\cdot1$	$221\cdot7\pm0\cdot1$
	Mass susceptibility at $T = 293$ K		
	($J\ T^{-2}\ kg^{-1}$)		(emu g^{-1})
tantalum	$(0\cdot8490\pm0\cdot0006)\times10^{-2}$		$(0\cdot8490\pm0\cdot0006)\times10^{-6}$
palladium	$(5\cdot231\pm0\cdot004)\times10^{-2}$		$(5\cdot231\pm0.004)\times10^{-6}$

4.2 Measurement of paramagnetic susceptibility

The force method is the one which is used most in measuring paramagnetic susceptibility. The chief difference from Section 4.1.3 is that the forces are smaller and therefore greater sensitivity is required in the force measurement.

If we write

$$\sigma_x = \chi B_0^x \text{ in Equations (4.2) we get}$$

$$F = m\chi B_0^x dB_0^x/dz$$

The force is therefore greatest when $B_0^x dB_0^x/dz$ is at a maximum. In an electromagnet this is usually near the edge of the pole gap (Fig. 4.6).

In this form susceptibilities are not measured absolutely, since $B_0^x dB_0^x dz$ is almost impossible to measure accurately. For relative measurements various standards of susceptibility are used depending on the range of sensitivity for which the balance is designed. Two of them are Ta and Pd, both in pure metallic form (see Table 4.1).

4.2.1 The Gouy method

This is a variant of the force method which permits absolute measurement of paramagnetic susceptibility in long, thin, uniform specimens that are absolutely free from ferromagnetic contamination.

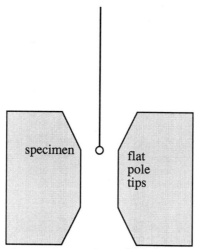

Figure 4.6 Specimen position for the measurement of susceptibility by the force method.

For a uniform paramagnetic specimen, the vertical force on a small element of length dz (Fig. 4.7) is

$$dF_z = dm\,\chi\,B_0^x\,dB_0^x/dz$$
$$= 1/2(\rho\,\alpha\,dz\,\chi)\,d(B_0^x)^2/dz$$
$$F_z = 1/2\chi\,\alpha\,\rho\,[(B_0^x)_1^2 - (B_0^x)_2^2] \tag{4.3}$$

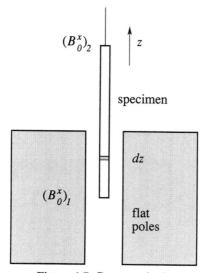

Figure 4.7 Gouy method.

When the specimen length is adequate $(B_0^x)^2_{\frac{1}{2}}$ may be neglected. Since the area of cross section α and the density ρ may be measured accurately the susceptibility χ is given absolutely.

4.2.2 Effect of ferromagnetic impurities on the measurement of paramagnetic susceptibility

The test for the presence of ferromagnetic contamination in a paramagnetic sample is to measure the apparent susceptibility χ_{app} in different field strengths. In a pure paramagnet the susceptibility is independent of field.

When a small fraction x of a ferromagnetic impurity is present, the magnetization of which is σ per unit mass, the apparent susceptibility of the whole specimen is

$$\chi_{app} = (1-x)\chi + x\sigma/B_0 \tag{4.4}$$

where χ is the true susceptibility of the paramagnetic component.

Thus a graph is plotted of χ_{app} against $(B_0)^{-1}$. The true susceptibility is indicated by the intercept at $(B_0)^{-1} = 0$, since $(1-x)$ rarely differs much from unity.

This correction will not work for the Gouy method, since different parts of the specimen are situated in different but undefined fields. Nor will it work for superparamagnets, for which the apparent susceptibility depends to some extent on field.

4.3 Dipole moment methods – SQUIDS

Any magnetic dipole, whether ferromagnetic or paramagnetic, produces a field of the order of

$$B_0 = M/d^3$$

in its vicinity, where M is the dipole moment and d is the distance of the point on the field from the centre of the dipole. If d can be fixed, measuring the field leads to a knowledge of the dipole moment and hence its magnetization or its susceptibility.

A variety of methods has been used to measure this dipole field but except for one relatively new method the attainable sensitivity was usually not good enough. The new method is to use the SQUID. It is useful to digress here to see how this device works.

4.3.1 SQUID magnetometry

SQUID stands for Superconducting Quantum Interference Device.

We assume knowledge of some basic properties of superconductors. These are:

(a) That Cooper pairs exist. These are electrons coupled together in a special way so that the pair cannot give up or receive energy continuously. It is only possible when the energy exceeds a definite limit, of the order of kT_c, where T_c is the superconducting transition temperature. This means that Cooper pairs cannot be attenuated by normal lattice scattering and therefore the electrical resistivity of the sample of solid containing them is zero.

(b) A Cooper pair has mass $2m$ and charge $2e$ and it can be considered to act as though it is a single particle. Its associated quantum (de Broglie) wave is thus appropriate to the mass $2m$.

Because of the absence of scattering the quantum wave of the quasi-particle retains phase coherence over long distances. The long coherence length is the basis of the properties we use here.

The wave function is of the form $\Psi_p = A \exp\{2\pi i/h\,(\boldsymbol{P}.\boldsymbol{r})\}$, where $\boldsymbol{P}$ is the total momentum. In a given superconductor, for uniform current density, all Cooper pairs have the same wavelength. They have fixed momentum, which may sometimes be zero.

4.3.2 The phase of a pair wave

Simplifying the model to one dimension we write the wave function in the form

$$\Psi_p = \sin 2\pi(\chi/\lambda - vt)$$

where the wavelength λ is given by $\lambda P = h$, in which P is the momentum.

Consider two points X and Y that are separated. When there is no current the momentum is zero and the wavelength is infinite. X and Y are then equal phase points.

When P is finite the phase difference is

$$(\Delta\phi)_{XY} = (\phi_X - \phi_Y) = 2\pi \int_X^Y x/\lambda \,.\, dl$$

where x is a unit vector in the propagation direction. It may be shown that this phase difference is given by

$$(\Delta\phi)_{XY} = (4\pi m)/(hn_se) \int_X^Y \boldsymbol{J} \,.\, dl \tag{4.5}$$

where $\boldsymbol{J}$ is the current density and n_s is the density of electrons.

Thus the phase difference may be controlled and adjusted by altering the current density.

4.3.3 Effect of a magnetic field

The application of a magnetic field changes the quantization condition, by adding a new term to the equation for the momentum.

In this case we write

$$P = 2mv + 2eA$$

where A is the magnetic vector potential.

Since $\lambda P = h$, the wavelength λ must depend on A and therefore on the field. This leads to a new equation.

$$(\Delta\phi)_{XY} = (4\pi m)/hn_s e)\int_X^Y \boldsymbol{J}.\mathbf{dl} + (4\pi e)/h\int_X^Y \boldsymbol{A}.\mathbf{dl} \tag{4.6}$$

The first term on the right hand side is due to the current and the second term is due to the field. We can alter the phase by changes in the magnetic field.

4.3.4 Circular conductor

Now let the supercurrent flow in a closed circuit (Fig. 4.8). The Cooper wave must join up in the circuit, leading to the expectation that only certain phase differences will be allowed and thus there are restrictions on the allowed combinations of $\boldsymbol{J}$ and $\boldsymbol{A}$. That is $\Delta\phi = 2\pi n$, where n is an integer. This is the phase condition, or quantum condition, which quantizes the allowed combination of field and current.

$$(\Delta\phi)_J + \int_S \boldsymbol{B}.\mathbf{d}S = nh/2e$$

where B is the induction and $\mathbf{d}S$ is an element of area. This quantity is called the fluxoid Φ'.

The fluxon, or quantum of flux, is the smallest step in this

$$= \Phi_0 = h/2e$$
$$= 2 \cdot 07 \times 10^{-15}\, \text{T m}^2 = \text{weber}.$$

Thus if we can detect the phase differences we have an extremely sensitive sensor for magnetic flux.

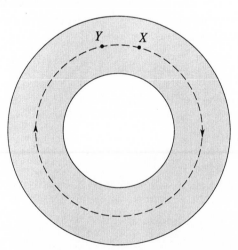

Figure 4.8 Circular superconducting path.

4.3.5 Quantum interference

It is possible for Cooper pairs to tunnel as pairs through very thin insulating layers of the order of 10^{-9} m thick (Fig. 4.9), retaining phase coherence. This tunnelling supercurrent can flow even in the absence of a driving potential. Its magnitude depends on the phase difference across the barrier.

The current is given by

$$i = i_c \sin(\phi_Q - \phi_P) \tag{4.7}$$

where i_c is a constant characteristic of the barrier and $(\phi_Q - \phi_P)$ is the phase difference across the barrier.

Thus measuring the current through a weak link gives a measure of the quantum mechanical phase difference between the ends.

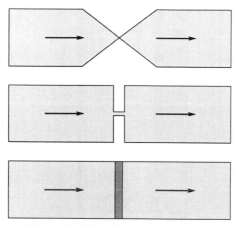

Figure 4.9 Three kinds of weak link.

4.3.6 Quantum interferometer

The system shown in Figure 4.10 is the quantum mechanical equivalent of Young's slits in optics. The circuit is made up of superconducting material and X and Y are weak links. The supercurrent flowing at W divides, part going via X and part going via Y and then recombines at Z. The route via X is left unchanged while Y is subjected to varying magnetic fields and thus to a varying phase angle. The quantum waves are coherent and the recombined wave at Z reflects the differing phases between the X and Y routes. This controls the magnitude of the supercurrent at Z. Measuring this current as a function of applied field at Y gives a graph such as Figure 4.11. Counting the 'fringes' and also following the structure of the current within the fringes gives a sensitive measure of the magnetic field strength at Y.

This leads to a very sensitive magnetometer, called the SQUID mag-

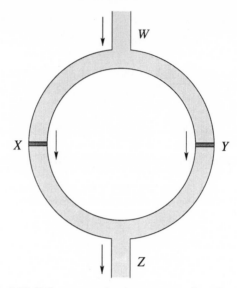

Figure 4.10 DC superconducting quantum interferometer.

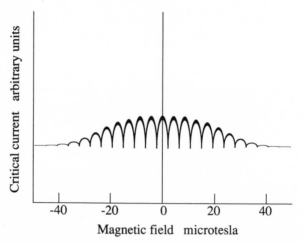

Figure 4.11 output current of the DC quantum interferometer changing as the field difference between the two arms is varied.

netometer. In practice there are refinements and developments that make it reliable and convenient to use but these are not covered here. A typical working arrangement for measuring susceptibility at low temperature is illustrated schematically in Figure 4.12.

Limiting sensitives for the method are indicated in Table 4.2. It is easily the most sensitive instrument for measuring field strengths, magnetizations and susceptibilities. Its disadvantages are that the sensor must be main-

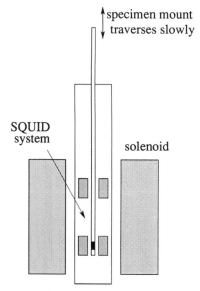

Figure 4.12 Schematic SQUID magnetometer.

tained at a constant, very low temperature and the problem of screening against the unwanted influence of stray external magnetic fields is not trivial.

Table 4.2 Sensitivity of SQUID magnetometer for 1 g samples

	cgs/emu	SI
Specific magnetization	10^{-8}	10^{-8}
Mass susceptibility	10^{-12}	10^{-8}
Field	10^{-8}	10^{-12}
Induction	10^{-15}	10^{-19}

4.4 Derivation of spontaneous magnetization from experimental data

A typical set of experimental data, on pure nickel, for the dependence of magnetization on field at different temperatures is shown in Figure 4.13. If the measured magnetization is essentially independent of field at low temperatures the measured values are certainly intrinsic. The linear extrapolation to where the internal field (applied field corrected for demagnetizing field) is zero gives the value of the spontaneous magnetization for the temperature at which the measurements were made. The same

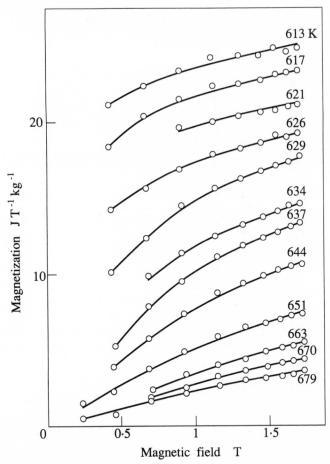

Figure 4.13 Magnetic isothermals for nickel near the Curie temperature.

procedure can then be followed at higher temperatures, still remote from the Curie temperature.

Near T_C the isothermal (σ, B_0) graphs are curved and difficult to extrapolate to $B_0 = 0$. It is helpful to construct graphs of B_0 against T for constant σ, by interpolation from a graph such as Figure 4.13.

More temperatures are required than are shown in Figure 4.13. Figure 4.14 shows such a set of curves of constant magnetization. The temperature for which the magnetization of a given line is the spontaneous magnetization is the extrapolation to where $B_0 = 0$. This is not strictly an exact procedure but it introduces little error for a homogeneous ferromagnet at temperatures within a few degrees of T_C (so that $T/T_C < 0.98$). A better measurement uses the magnetocaloric effect, but this is slow and difficult to measure.

At low temperatures $(T/T_C < 0.1)$ the spontaneous magnetization is

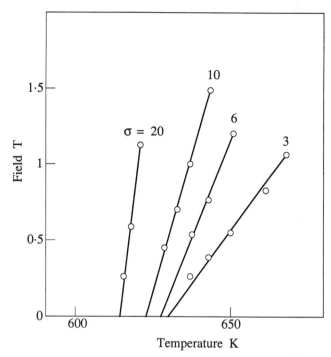

Figure 4.14 Curves of constant magnetization for nickel (derived from Figure 4.13).

expected from spin wave theory to vary according to the law

$$\sigma_T/\sigma_0 = 1 - A(T/T_C)^{3/2} \tag{4.8}$$

where A is a constant of proportionality. Thus the saturation magnetic moment, the value of the spontaneous magnetization at zero temperature, is obtained by plotting graphs of the spontaneous magnetization against $T^{3/2}$ and extrapolating them to where $T = 0$. It is useful if the lowest temperature of measurement is not higher than $0 \cdot 05\ T$.

When the measured magnetization varies markedly with field at all temperatures it is never certain that it is the intrinsic magnetization that is being measured. The variation of magnetization with field might be due to domain effects and the interpretation is more difficult. If no better information is available an approximation to the zero temperature saturation magnetization can sometimes be obtained by extrapolating the measured magnetization to its value for $(B_0)^{-1} = 0$ at each temperature and then extrapolating these values against either $T^{3/2}$ or T^2 to $T = 0$.

4.4.1 Measurement of Curie temperature

The Curie temperature of a ferromagnet is not obviously identified in a superficial examination of the results of magnetization measurements, because of the disturbing influence of the field which must be applied to align the domains. Strictly speaking, a sharp second order phase transition only exists when there is no field. The procedure which follows is called either the Arrott method or the Belov and Goryaga method.

Near the Curie temperature the reduced magnetization $\sigma_{B,T}/\sigma_{0,0}$ is fairly small. It is argued that under these conditions differences in the applicability of different models of ferromagnetism are not great and it is sufficient to adapt the simple theory of a local moment ferromagnet. Here the quantities analogous to the molecular field coefficient γ and the atomic magnetic moment μ are not fundamental, being more of the nature of empirical constants.

Adapting Equation (2.8) (with $J = 1/2$) we write

$$(\sigma_{B,T}/\sigma_{0,0}) = \tanh((B + \gamma\sigma_{B,T})\mu/kT) \tag{4.9}$$

Thus

$$(\mu/kT)(B_0 + \gamma\sigma_{B,T}) = \tanh^{-1}(\sigma_{B,T}/\sigma_{0,0})$$
$$= (\sigma_{B,T}/\sigma_{0,0}) + 1/3(\sigma_{B,T}/\sigma_{0,0})^3 + 1/5(\sigma_{B,T}/\sigma_{0,0})^5 \tag{4.10}$$

which tends to $(\sigma_{B,T}/\sigma_{0,0})$ when $T \rightarrow T_C$

That is,

$$T = (\mu\sigma_{0,0}/k)(B_0/\sigma_{B,T} + \gamma)$$

At $T = T_C$ the reciprocal of the susceptibility $(B_0/\sigma_{B,T})$ is zero or very small. Thus $\gamma = kT_C/\mu\sigma_{0,0}$.

For temperatures near but not necessarily equal to T_C

$$\mu B_0/kT = \sigma_{B,T}/\sigma_{0,0} - \sigma_{B,T}/\sigma_{0,0} \cdot T_C/T + 1/3(\sigma_{B,T}/\sigma_{0,0})^3 \tag{4.11}$$

or

$$(B_0/\sigma_{B,T}) = (kT/3\mu\sigma_{0,0}^3)\sigma_{B,T}^2 + (k/\mu\sigma_{0,0})(T - T_C) \tag{4.12}$$
$$= AT\sigma_{B,T}^2 + C(T - T_C) \tag{4.13}$$

where A and C are constants characteristic of the material.

Thus we expect graphs of $(B_0/\sigma_{B,T})$ against $\sigma_{B,T}^2$ at constant temperature to be linear. Their intercept on the axis, where $\sigma_{B,T}^2 = 0$, gives

$$(B_0/\sigma_{B,T})_0 = C(T - T_C) \tag{4.14}$$

which varies linearly with T, having a zero value when $T = T_C$. Figure 4.15 illustrates the procedure.

The method may only be used fairly close to T_C and in fields which are not too high, or the conditions of the approximations will not hold. Also, it is not applicable to heterogeneous systems having more than a single Curie temperature.

A rough approximation to the Curie temperature that is good enough for many purposes can be measured quite simply. The magnetization is measured as a function of temperature in a constant field (say of the order of 0·2 T, or 2000 Oe). Where the graph of magnetization against tempera-

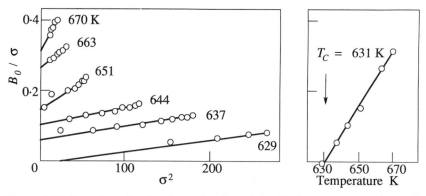

Figure 4.15 Procedure for the determination of the Curie temperature (Arrott). The data are for nickel.

ture goes through a point of inflection is usually within ± 10 K of the true Curie temperature.

4.5 The generation of magnetic fields

Magnetic fields are always generated by the magnetic effects of electric currents. Sometimes the effect of the current is indirect, being used to magnetize a permanent magnet which is then used independently. The problems in producing magnetic fields are usually one or more of the following.

(a) Making the field strong enough. The need is to optimize the magnetic effects of the electric current, and thus to concentrate the electrical energy into a volume as small as possible without creating intolerable problems from Joule heating.
(b) Making the field sufficiently uniform over distance, or otherwise introducing some controlled spatial variation of the field such as a gradient.
(c) Making the field sufficiently stable over an acceptable period of time. If Joule heat is not removed adequately or its effects compensated, the temperature and thus the resistance of the wire carrying the current will vary with time.

It is often very difficult to solve all these problems at the same time.

4.5.1 Solenoid magnets with air core

Most coil systems that are used to generate strong magnetic fields are composed of circular windings. The field produced by a system may be calculated by superposing the field contributions of all the separate turns. The unit in this calculation is a single circular current. In this section it is convenient to deal with the magnetic excitation H, measured in SI units $(A\,m^{-1})$.

The field B_0 (in T) is given by $B_0 = \mu_0 H$.

In cgs units $\mu_0 = 1$.

The value of H along the axis of a single circular current at a distance z from the plane of the current is

$$H_z = (i\rho^2)/[2(z^2 + \rho^2)^{3/2}] \tag{4.15}$$

where i is the current and ρ is the radius of the current.

For points off the axis the calculation of the field is more complicated but it is straightforward and well documented. When a field is required that is homogeneous along the axis a system of two or more coaxial coils may be devised for which the derivative of the field at the central point is zero.

Practical solenoids are usually of finite thickness and length, made up of many turns of relatively thin wire wound uniformly within a rectangular cross section (Fig. 4.16).

If the wire is wound uniformly the current density τ is the same at any point within the winding space. The actual current at that point is $\tau d\sigma$. Taking the dimensional parameters as defined in Figure 4.16, the value of

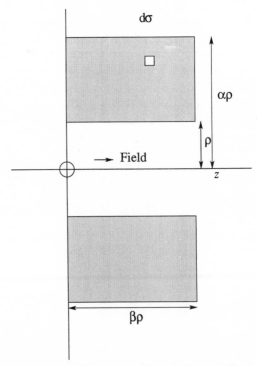

Figure 4.16 Model for the calculation of the field due to a uniform solenoid. α and β are defined by this diagram.

H at the origin is given by

$$H_z(0) = \tau \rho F_1 \tag{4.16}$$

where F_1 is a geometrical factor

$$F_1 = 1/2\beta \ln \left[\frac{\alpha + (\alpha^2 + \beta^2)^{1/2}}{1 + (1 + \beta^2)^{1/2}} \right] \tag{4.17}$$

Values of F_1 are easy to compute, or they may be read from tables. Equivalent expressions may be used for the field gradient

$$H'_z(0) = \tau F_2 \tag{4.18}$$

where F_2 is similarly tabulated.

The procedure for estimating the field on the axis away from the centre of a coil is illustrated in the following example. The dimensions of the solenoid are given in Figure 4.17. The windings are regular, there being 5 turns per centimetre in both the radial and the axial directions. That is, $\tau = 25 \times 10^4 \, i \, \text{A m}^{-2}$.

From the diagram, $\rho_1 = 0.02$ m. For part a of the coil, $\alpha = 6/2 = 3$ and $\beta_a = 4.5$. For these parameters (Equation (4.17)), $F_1(\alpha, \beta_a) = 0.9106$. For part b of the coil, $\alpha = 3$ and $\beta_b = 2.5$, for which $F_1(\alpha, \beta_b) = 0.7824$. That is,

$$H_z = 0.02 \, \tau \, (0.9106 + 0.7824) = 0.03386 \, \tau = 8465 \, i \, \text{A m}^{-1}.$$

This is equivalent to $B_0 = 1.064 \times 10^{-2} \, i$ T or $1.064 \times 10^2 \, i$ Oe.

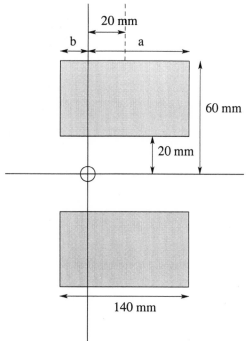

Figure 4.17 Dimensions of a uniform solenoid.

This model is applicable to low-power conventional solenoids, and also to superconducting solenoids. In many cases the dissipation of large amounts of power is a serious problem, which is considered in Section 4.5.2. One way of getting better cooling efficiency is to make a thick solenoid of single turns shaped out of copper sheets. The form of each turn, or pancake, is shown in Figure 4.18.

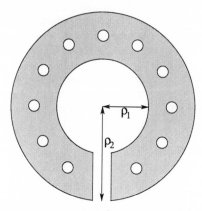

Figure 4.18 Single turn of Bitter solenoid (pancake).

Here the length of the current path is least in the centre and greatest on the outside, being proportional to the radius ρ. The effective resistance of the path is likewise proportional to ρ. That is, since the ends of the turns are equipotential surfaces the current density is proportional to ρ^{-1}.

When a helix is made out of a collection of such pancakes by suitable cutting, stacking and joining together, a Bitter solenoid is produced.

The analytical treatment for this case is broadly similar to that for the uniform solenoid. τ_0 is now the current density at the inner edge, so that

$$\tau = (\tau_0/\rho)\rho_1$$

The geometrical coefficients K_1 and K_2 are again tabulated, so that

$$H_z(0) = \tau_0\rho K_1 \tag{4.19}$$

and

$$H'_z(0) = \tau_0 K_2 \tag{4.20}$$

and using the tables the calculation is the same as for the uniform solenoid.

4.5.2 Power consumption and dissipation in a solenoid

Let the uniform solenoid considered in Section 4.5.1 be made from wire having a resistivity η, and let the body of the coil be occupied to a fraction λ by the actual conductor, the rest of the volume being used as insulation, interspaces between turns and cooling medium. The whole coil contains N turns. Thus the area density of turns

$$= dN/d\sigma = N/[(\alpha - 1)\beta\rho^2] \tag{4.21}$$

The resistance of the element of coil for which $d\sigma$ is the cross sectional area is

$$dR = \frac{2\pi\eta\rho}{\lambda} \frac{dN}{d\sigma/dN} = \frac{2\pi\eta\rho}{\lambda} (dN/d\sigma)^2 d\sigma \tag{4.22}$$

or, putting $d\sigma = d\rho\, dz$ we have

$$dR = \frac{2\pi\eta N^2}{\lambda(\alpha - 1)^2\beta^2\rho^4} \rho\, d\rho\, dz \tag{4.23}$$

By integration the resistance of the whole coil becomes

$$R = \frac{\pi\eta N^2(\alpha + 1)}{\lambda\beta\rho_1(\alpha - 1)} \tag{4.24}$$

The current density is given by $\tau = \dfrac{iN}{(\alpha - 1)\beta\rho_1^2}$ (4.25)

where i is the current. If the steady state power consumption is $W = i^2 R$ we have

$$\tau = \frac{1}{\rho_1}\left[\frac{W\lambda}{\eta\rho_1}\right]^{1/2}\left[\frac{1}{\pi\beta(\alpha^2 - 1)}\right]^{1/2} \tag{4.26}$$

This value for τ may now be substituted in Equation (4.16) to give

$$H_z(0) = \left[\frac{W\lambda}{\eta\rho_1}\right]^{1/2} G_1 \tag{4.27}$$

where G_1 is a wholly geometrical factor given by

$$G_1 = \left[\frac{1}{\pi\beta(\alpha^2 - 1)}\right]^{1/2} F_1 \tag{4.28}$$

Values of G_1 for different α and β are available in tabulated form.

Obtaining the highest possible field for a given expenditure of power (and thus of cooling capacity) is then a question of finding the shape of the coil having the highest value of G_1. For a uniform solenoid of the kind considered $(G_1)_{max} = 0 \cdot 142$, and this occurs for that shape for which $\alpha = 3$ and β lies between -2 and $+2$.

The highest G_1 for a Bitter coil is $0 \cdot 166$ (17 per cent improvement) and another such single turn solenoid using pancake turns of variable thickness gives $(G_1)_{max} = 0 \cdot 185$ (30 per cent improvement on a uniform solenoid).

It is instructive to calculate the order of maximum field that might be expected from a given solenoid. Consider a Bitter solenoid of optimum shape, so that $G_1 = 0 \cdot 166$, having an internal radius (which controls the size of the working space available in the field being produced) of 300 mm. The packing factor $\lambda = 0\cdot5$ and the maximum power W available is 1 MW. Let the pancakes be made of copper of resistivity $\eta = 2 \times 10^{-8}$ ohm m. Then the largest value of H available is

$$H_z(0) = G_1(W\lambda/\eta\rho_1)^{1/2} = 4\cdot79 \times 10^6 \text{ A m}^{-1}.$$ The equivalent field

is $B_0 = \mu_0 H = 6\cdot0$ T (or 60 kOe).

If the temperature of the conducting material rises as a result of Joule heating, field stability with respect to time is lost, unless electronic stabilization of the current is used. When the current density exceeds 3×10^6 A m^{-2} (300 A cm^{-2}) a cooling device is usually built into the solenoid. This has the effect of reducing the packing factor λ. For conventional solenoids various methods of cooling are listed in Table 4.3.

Table 4.3 Solenoids for production of fields

Fields up to about (T)	(Oe)	Type
10^{-2}	10^2	Cooling by natural convection
10^{-1}	10^3	Cooling plates inserted within the coils
1	10^4	Tubular conductors with coolant flow inside
10	10^5	Bitter type, axial coolant tubes
10	10^5	Superconducting solenoids, elements in liquid He
100	10^6	Pulsed fields

4.5.3 Mechanical effects in solenoids

The current in the windings of a solenoid reacts mechanically with the field and when the field is strong the forces are very appreciable. The equivalent stress on the outermost turns of wire can well exceed the tensile strength of copper wire, causing failure (which might be explosive) if the turns are unsupported. Special construction is often employed to avoid this, and windings of higher tensile strength are sometimes used.

Considerable amounts of energy are stored in energized magnets. The magnetic energy per unit volume is $1/2HB$. For a field of 10 T (100 kOe), equivalent to $H = 7\cdot96 \times 10^6$ A m^{-1}, the potential energy is $3\cdot98 \times 10^7$ J m^{-3}. (For comparison, the explosive power of T N T is about 6×10^9 J m^{-3}.)

In all energized magnet systems a safety device is inserted into the power supply, often a high impedance resistive load connected in parallel, so that in the event of sudden interruption of the current the magnetic energy can be dissipated relatively slowly.

4.5.4 Superconducting solenoids

If the solenoid is wound from wire made from a hard superconductor most of the problems to do with the dissipation of Joule heat are avoided. This leads to what is perhaps the simplest method of producing fairly large fields, so long as the required field stability is not great.

Fundamental properties of superconductors define their eligibility as materials for making solenoid magnets. Each material has a critical temperature above which it becomes normal. The critical temperatures of viable hard superconductors are between 10 K and 25 K, limiting the operating temperature to about 4 K or lower. At a chosen operating temperature there is a critical magnetic field above which the wire becomes normally conducting.

This is greater than 10 T (100 kOe) for many materials that are commercially available. For given conditions of field and temperature there is a current density above which the normal state is reached. Critical current densities are typically about 10^9 A m^{-2} (10^5 A cm^{-2}).

The hardest known superconductor at the present time is the alloy Nb$_3$Sn. It has very poor mechanical strength. Other alloys that are used are NbZr, NbTi and V$_3$Ga. The design of superconducting magnets is often complicated by the inner turns seeing a higher field than those on the outside. The current tends to go critical selectively according to position within the coil, and composite construction is sometimes used to allow for this so that a higher current density can be tolerated on the outside of the coil, or alternatively a material having a higher critical field may be used on the inside.

If a superconducting solenoid is working near its limit and it goes normal suddenly a large amount of stored energy is released and a violent explosion will occur if precautions are not taken. The stored magnetic energy could be augmented by that from a consequent rapid and violent evaporation of liquid helium from the cooling bath.

It is common to clad superconducting wire with a coating of a low resistance normal conductor. If the superconductor goes normal a (reduced) current is carried locally by the cladding, increasing the time constant of the breakdown. In modern applications the superconductor is drawn down into very fine filaments within a copper matrix, the resistance of which is high compared with that of the superconductor. The mechanical properties of the whole wire are much improved and flux jumps and other instabilities tend to disappear. A typical commercial superconducting magnet made from filamentary NbTi will produce fields of about 8 T (80 kOe) when operated at a temperature of 4·2 K and just over 10 T (100 kOe) at 2·2 K.

4.5.5 Iron-cored electromagnets

Iron-cored electromagnets are often used when moderate field strengths are required. The power requirements are usually quite modest, and good control of spatial and time variation of the field can be obtained fairly easily.

In a closed magnetic circuit (Fig. 4.19) we may write

$$i = \oint \boldsymbol{H} . \mathrm{d}\boldsymbol{l} \qquad (4.29)$$

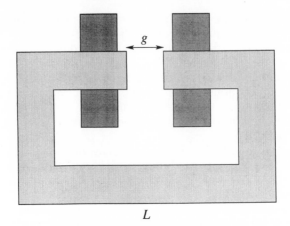

Figure 4.19 Simple electromagnet.

where i is the total current looping the magnetic circuit, found by multiplying the number of turns of wire by the current in each. The quantity $\oint H . dl$ is known as the magnetomotive force (MMF), by analogy with the electrical circuit where $E dl$ is called the electromotive force. In the same circuit the sum $\Sigma(l/\mu_r A)$ is called the reluctance, analogous to electrical resistance. The qualities l, μ_r and A refer respectively to the length, relative permeability and area of cross section of each component in the magnetic path. We may now write for the total flux in the circuit

$\Phi = (MMF)/(\text{reluctance})$.

The flux at a point is given by $\Phi = BA$, where B is the induction (that is, the flux density). Also, $B = \mu_r \mu_0 H = \mu_r B_0$ so that $\Phi = \mu_r B_0 A$. Thus, in a magnetic circuit of constant area of cross section having a length of iron L and g the length of an air gap, the field is given by

$$B_0 = \frac{i}{(L/\mu_r A) + g} \tag{4.30}$$

When the permeability of the iron μ_r is very much greater than unity (usually it is of the order of 10^4) it is the length of the air gap that dominates the performance of the magnet. The design is complicated by the permeability of iron varying with the field, and there are leakage effects.

Pole tips (Fig. 4.20) are often introduced adjacent to the air gap in order to concentrate the flux and so increase the field. These are truncated cones with an optimum cone semi-angle of just under 60 degrees. For the largest fields the saturation magnetization of the pole tips should be as large as possible. In this case an iron–cobalt alloy having a high saturation magnetization is used, but this material is difficult to demagnetize. Where a versatile and stable performance is more important than the highest possible field pole tips of soft iron are usually used.

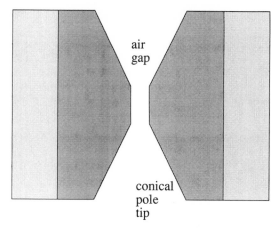

Figure 4.20 Conical pole tips.

The maximum effect from the ferromagnetic core of the magnet is achieved when the pole tips are saturated. There is no gain in making the magnet bigger beyond this point, except to provide better field uniformity or a larger working volume.

In most electromagnets the energizing coils are placed near to the pole gap and they contribute directly to the field, their direct contribution being then at least equal to that coming directly from the iron core. A point is reached eventually when the use of the iron core ceases to be worthwhile. The space occupied by the iron is better filled with turns of the conductor.

Some electromagnets employ a field stabilizing device in the form of a Hall effect probe placed in the field, the output from which is processed and fed back to the circuit energizing the magnet, thereby controlling it. Stabilities of the order of 1 part in 10^6 are possible in this way, in fields of about 1 T (10 kOe).

4.5.6 Pulsed magnetic fields

The limits for obtaining strong magnetic fields using non-superconducting magnets (superconducting magnets have different limitations) are mechanical strength and the dissipation of Joule heat. If field pulses of short duration are used the Joule heat need not be removed. It may be stored acceptably within the thermal capacity of the coil. The usable length of pulse $(t_m - t_0)$ is limited by the relationship

$$\int_{t_0}^{t_m} \eta(T)[\tau(t)]^2 \, dt < \int_{T_0}^{T_1} c(T) \, dT \tag{4.31}$$

The current density $\tau(t)$ and the specific heat capacity $c(T)$ refer to unit volume of the coil material. The resistance $\eta(T)$ is usually a fairly simple function of the temperature T. T_0 is the starting temperature of the coil. There are obvious benefits in making T_0 as low as possible. T_1 is the highest tolerable final temperature. It is set by the degree of damage which can be accepted in the coil. In the limit T_1 is the melting temperature of the wire or the temperature at which its insulation breaks down.

The method is to start with a source of stored energy (called the tank) such as a capacitor, a battery bank or a rotating dynamo. Let the available energy be E_t. During the pulse operation part of this energy is used in setting up the field and part is lost in Joule heat.

$$E_t = \int_{t_0}^{t_m} Ri^2 \, dt + \int_{t_0}^{t_m} (d\phi/dt)i \, dt \tag{4.32}$$

The flux is given by

$\phi = Li$, where L is the inductance of the coil. That is,

$$E_t = \int_{t_0}^{t_m} Ri^2 \, dt + \int_{0}^{t_m} Li \, di + \int_{t_0}^{t_m} (dL/dt)i^2 \, dt \tag{4.33}$$

In most cases a situation is aimed for in which the coil is rigid and where the current distribution within it does not change with time during the pulse. That is, where the third term in Equation (4.33) is zero because $(dL/dt) = 0$. The second term in Equation (4.33) is the useful magnetic energy E_m, equal to $1/2Li_m^2$, where i_m is the maximum current in the pulse.

The efficiency κ of the pulse operation is E_m/E_t. This is made less favourable when the third term of Equation (4.33) is not zero but positive. This usually happens to some extent because the coil tends to stretch as a result of the very large mechanical forces acting on it and the current is also pushed outwards within the conductor. Both effects tend to make dL/dt positive.

The field produced at the centre of the coil is given very roughly by

$$B_0 = S(E_m \mu_0 / V)^{1/2} \tag{4.34}$$

V is the effective volume of the coil and S is a geometrical factor depending on the shape of the coil. Its value is best (approaching unity) when the coil is long and narrow. E_m is often about 5000 J. Fields of the order of 50 T (500 kOe) have been produced in pulses lasting for about 10^{-3} seconds.

Explosive pulse methods can be used to obtain still higher field strengths. If dL/dt can be made large and negative by shrinking the coil explosively during the current pulse (see Equation (4.33)) a large magnification of the field is possible. As an example, in one experiment a coil made of 10 swg copper wire wound with 3 turns per inch was capable of producing a pulsed field of 9 T when used in a particular circuit. When it was explosively compressed to about one tenth of its original diameter within 10 μs during the electrical pulse, a field of 1400 T (14×10^6 Oe) was produced over a sphere of about 6 mm diameter, lasting for several microseconds. This is of limited application since it is fairly difficult to complete many measurements reliably during such short measuring times, and not many physical properties are immune from being perturbed by the pressures involved.

4.6 The measurement of magnetic field

First we consider the measurement of field in free space or in air. The induction B is given by

$$B = \mu_r B_0 = \mu_r \mu_0 H \tag{4.35}$$

μ_r is the relative permeability of the medium and this is very nearly unity for air. The flux ϕ crossing an area A is

$$\phi = BA \tag{4.36}$$

Thus measurement of the flux leads to a knowledge of the field.

4.6.1 Measurement of magnetic flux

Let a search coil of area A be placed in a magnetic field, so that a flux Φ is enclosed. When the flux is changed by switching off the field, by removing the coil or by turning the coil so that it encloses no flux, an emf is produced across the ends of the coil which is related to the change in flux.

$$e = -\sum d\Phi/dt$$

or,

$$\sum \Phi = BA = -\int_0^t e \, dt \tag{4.37}$$

An integrating device is required, to measure $\int e \, dt$ over the time of the flux change. Examples are: (a) the ballistic galvanometer, (b) the moving coil fluxmeter, or (c) an electronic integrator (there are various kinds).

4.6.2 Ballistic galvanometer

This is simply a moving coil galvanometer having a long time of oscillation compared with the duration of the current pulse the time integral of which is being measured.

Calibration is required. The deflection is measured when a known impulse is imposed by reversal of a known current through a standard mutual inductance. There are other equivalent methods of calibration. Flux may then be measured by connecting a search coil of known area to the instrument and manipulating it in the field. The accuracy of the flux measured in this way can be much better than ± 1 per cent.

4.6.3 Fluxmeter

A moving coil fluxmeter is a galvanometer with the torque of its suspension so small as to be ineffective. There is strong electromagnetic damping and air damping of the coil is usually negligible. Angular momentum is imparted to the moving coil and electromagnetic damping stops the movement. The calibration of the instrument is independent of the suspension and since all the dimensions are fixed it remains constant. Instrument makers supply a fixed calibration. The resistance of the search coil has little effect. Drift of the zero reading of the instrument and thermal emfs can be troublesome and they need devices to control them.

The combination of search coil and fluxmeter can be seen as a flux-conserving system. The flux collected in the search coil transfers itself to the moving coil.

4.6.4 Electronic integrators

These do electronically exactly what has just been considered using electromagnetic–mechanical methods. Modern integrated electronic circuits make this the best method. A DC coupled amplifier is used which has a differential element in a feedback loop (Fig. 4.21).

Let the output be $y = Ae_0$

$$e_2 = D(dy/dt) \text{ and } e_0 = e_1 + e_2$$

That is,

$$y = Ae_1 + AD \, dy/dt \tag{4.38}$$

Rearranging and integrating with respect to time gives

$$y = -1/D \int e_1 \, dt + 1/AD \int y \, dt \tag{4.39}$$

The second term in Equation (4.39) is an error which is ideally to be made as small as possible by having large amplification A. If long times of integration are required (say, for example 10^3 seconds) the product AD must be large (about 10^6).

One form is the Cioffi integrator, although in its original form it did not actually use electronic parts. It used a galvanometer amplifier, with a mutual inductance as the differentiating device. A galvanometer amplifier consists of a primary galvanometer the light spot from which falls on a split photocell. The unbalanced output from the photocell is read on a secondary galvanometer.

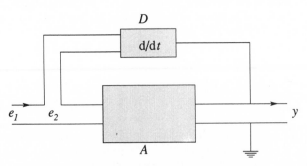

Figure 4.21 Electronic integrator.

4.6.5 Nuclear magnetic resonance

Nuclear magnetic resonance in magnetic materials is mentioned from a fundamental viewpoint in Chapter 8. Here we discuss its use to measure magnetic fields. The quantized energy levels of some nuclei in a magnetic field can be excited by high frequency radiation and the frequency of resonance may be used as a particularly sensitive and accurate measure of the field strength.

At resonance $\omega_0 = 2\pi f_0 = \pm\gamma B_0$ (4.40)

where γ is the gyromagnetic ratio for the nucleus used. Values of γ for protons, deuterons and Li nuclei are given in Table 4.4. Values of the quantity $G = 2\pi/\gamma$ are also given, where

field $= G \times$ (resonant frequency)   (4.41)

There are several ways of making the observation. One used in some commercial instruments is the Bloch method. There are three mutually perpendicular sets of coils; field modulating coils, transmitter coils and receiver coils (Fig. 4.22). A radio frequency generator feeds the transmitter coils, applying an alternating magnetic field perpendicular to the field

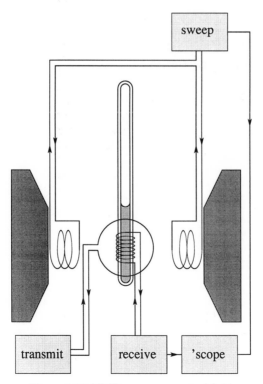

Figure 4.22 NMR measurement of field.

being measured. The nuclei being excited are contained in a sample tube within the coil system. If the nuclei are protons the sample is water. At resonance the sample radiates to the receiver coils, the signal from which is displayed. The coils are adjusted initially so as to minimize direct signal transfer from transmitter to receiver. A sweep device modulates the main field over a small amplitude about its steady value in order that the resonance condition may be recognized more easily.

The radio frequency signal is varied in frequency until resonance is found and then its frequency is measured. In accurate work an external crystal-controlled counter is used to measure the resonant frequency, and this may be calibrated against broadcast frequency standards. In the United Kingdom a very accurate standard is broadcast at a frequency of 200 kHz.

This method can be very sensitive. Under the most sensitive conditions the author has used it to detect changes of 2×10^{-7} T (0·002 Oe) in a field of 0·8 T (8 kOe). This is a sensitivity of 1 part in 4×10^6. The resonance condition is difficult to detect if the field is not very uniform. The smallest probes are about 5 mm in diameter and the field variation should not exceed 10^{-4} T (1 Oe) over this diameter.

A variation of the same method is to use electron spin resonance (ESR) instead of NMR. The value of γ for a free electron is several hundred times greater than that for a proton (see Table 4.4). Thus much weaker fields may be measured for the same resonant frequencies. A suitable material in which ESR may be observed is diphenyl picryl hydrazyl (DPPH). This is notable for its very sharp resonance. Values of the quantities γ and G for electrons are included in Table 4.4.

Table 4.4 Gyromagnetic ratios and conversion factors between resonant frequency and field

Nucleus	γ		G	
	$T^{-1}s^{-1}$	$Oe^{-1}s^{-1}$	$T\,s$	$Oe\,s$
^{1}H (proton)	$2 \cdot 6753 \times 10^8$	$2 \cdot 6753 \times 10^4$	$2 \cdot 3486 \times 10^{-8}$	$2 \cdot 3486 \times 10^{-4}$
^{2}D (deuteron)	$4 \cdot 1064 \times 10^7$	$4 \cdot 1064 \times 10^3$	$1 \cdot 5301 \times 10^{-7}$	$1 \cdot 5301 \times 10^{-3}$
^{7}Li	$1 \cdot 0396 \times 10^8$	$1 \cdot 0396 \times 10^4$	$6 \cdot 0438 \times 10^{-8}$	$6 \cdot 0438 = 10^{-4}$
electron (DPPH)	$1 \cdot 762 \times 10^{11}$	$1 \cdot 762 \times 10^7$	$3 \cdot 566 \times 10^{-11}$	$3 \cdot 566 \times 10^{-7}$

Frequency is measured in Hz

4.6.6 The Hall effect

When an electric current is passed through a conducting material placed in a magnetic field, in a direction perpendicular to the field, a Lorentz force acts on the conduction carriers which produces an emf in the third perpendicular direction. This is the Hall effect. The emf depends linearly on the field and can be used as a very convenient measure of field.

Various semiconducting compounds, such as InAs or InSb are good materials for probes, but their sensitivity depends rather sharply on temperature. Accurate control of temperature or electronic temperature compensation are necessary for accurate work.

4.6.7 Magnetoresistance

The electrical resistivity of conducting and semiconducting solids increases when a magnetic field is applied. This is called magnetoresistance and it may be used to measure field. The effect is not linear in field. In the most sensitive materials (a eutectic compound of InSb and NiSb is very sensitive) the influence of temperature is rather large. This gives a convenient but not very accurate measure of field. The main advantage is the very small field probes that are possible. One application is in making detectors for reading out information from magnetic bubble arrays.

4.6.8 The measurement of pulsed fields

Pulsed fields may be measured by using a search coil placed in a fixed position in the field. The instantaneous emf produced across the search coil is $e(t) \propto dB_0/dt$, and thus the field is proportional to the time integral of $e(t)$. An electronic integrator may therefore be used to estimate the field. Since the exact output depends on the shape of the pulse and other factors it is necessary to calibrate the measurement in situ with reference to some known phenomenon within the field range being covered.

4.6.9 Field measurement within a magnetized body – the magnetic potentiometer

It is often necessary to measure the field $(B_0)_i$ present inside a ferro-magnetic body when a demagnetizing field is acting. When the demagnetizing field is relatively large and difficult to estimate accurately, this is especially important. An example of this is in observing hysteresis loops on open-circuited samples. The magnetic potentiometer (sometimes called the Chattock potentiometer) is useful for doing this. This is shown in Figure 4.23.

The device consists of a coil long in relation to its diameter wound on to a non-magnetic core. The core is bent, typically into a semicircle, so that the ends of the coil lie in the same plane. The electrical ends of the coil must be taken from the same physical point. The coil diameter might be as small as 2 mm and the core diameter 15 mm, with about 100 turns of fine wire. The ends of the coil must lie flat on the ferromagnetic surface.

At any point the vector $\boldsymbol{H}$ and the magnetic scalar potential U are related by

$$\boldsymbol{H} = -\nabla U \tag{4.42}$$

The difference in potential between two points A and B (Fig. 4.23) is thus

$$U_A - U_B = \int_{\text{line}} \boldsymbol{H} . d\boldsymbol{l} \tag{4.43}$$

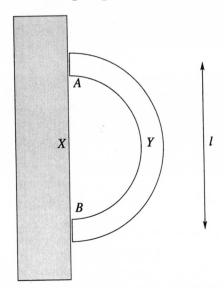

Figure 4.23 Chattock magnetic potentiometer.

If the closed path from A back to A via B, taking path X outwards through the specimen and returning along path Y outside, encloses no electric current

$$\int H.dl = 0$$

Thus

$$\int_X H.dl = \int_Y H.dl \tag{4.44}$$

When A and B are close together we can write for the inside path

$$\int_X H.dl = H_i l$$

where $H_i = (1/\mu_0)(B_0)_i$, and $(B_0)_i$ is the internal field in the specimen.
   For the path Y we consider the flux enclosed by the coil. This is

$$d\Phi = \int \alpha B_0 . dl \, n = \mu_0 n \alpha \int_Y H.dl \tag{4.45}$$

where n is the number of turns per unit length on the coil and α is its area of cross section. Thus

$$(B_0)_i = (1/n\alpha l)d\Phi \tag{4.46}$$

   The flux $d\Phi$ enclosed by the magnetic potentiometer may be measured using one of the integrating methods described in Section 4.6.1. The potentiometer is brought right up to the surface of the specimen from a

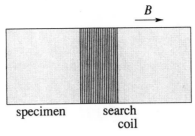

Figure 4.24 Measurement of magnetic induction in a solid specimen.

large distance away and the change in flux is measured. Usually the calibrating constant $(n\alpha l)^{-1}$ would be obtained by measurement in a known field.

4.6.10 Measurement of induction B

The induction B within a ferromagnetic specimen may be measured by wrapping a search coil of known total area A round the specimen (Fig. 4.24) and then measuring the change in flux when B is changed. When B is reversed from its saturation value B_s

$$\Delta\Phi = 2AB_s \qquad\qquad (4.47)$$

An integrating method is used to measure the change in flux. The search coil is often a few turns of insulated fine wire wound closely on to the specimen as a core.

Chapter 5 ⎯⎯⎯⎯⎯⎯⎯

Magnetic scattering of neutrons and magnetic excitations

5.1 Properties of the neutron

The important properties of the neutron for the examination of the structure of condensed matter are that it has no electric charge; that its mass is very closely the same as that of the proton; that its nuclear spin is one half; and that it possesses a magnetic moment.

Beams of neutrons for studying the properties of solid or liquid samples were first available from thermal neutron fission reactors. Their average energy is of the order of 0·025 eV, equivalent to an equilibrium temperature of about 300 K. This energy corresponds to a rather slow velocity of the order of 2700 ms^{-1}. A neutron thus takes about 10^{-13} s to traverse 3×10^{-10} m, roughly the diameter of a single atom. The wavelength λ association with a neutron of this energy may be calculated from the de Broglie relationship $\lambda = h/mv$. It is $1·5 \times 10^{-10}$ m. Since this wavelength is of similar magnitude to the interatomic spacing in atoms, diffraction effects are produced when neutrons are scattered by crystalline solids and these may be used to study the solids. Also, since the kinetic energies of thermal neutrons are of the same order as the energy quanta associated with lattice vibrations (phonons) and magnetic spin waves (magnons), the interchange of energy between thermal neutrons and phonons or magnons may be used as a basis for studying these properties. Another way of stating this is that the velocities of thermal neutrons are similar to the velocities of thermal and magnetic waves in crystals, allowing the possibility of measurable Doppler shifts for the scattered neutrons. The scattered neutrons undergo a displacement in energy. This experimental process is called inelastic neutron scattering.

Because of the absence of any electrostatic charge on the neutron, most materials are relatively transparent to neutrons and the scattering processes tend to be simple. All these advantages need to be offset against the relative difficulty of detecting neutrons. In addition neutron sources tend to be weak and very costly.

Thus there are similarities in the scattering of thermal neutrons and of X-rays by solid and liquid materials because their wavelengths are similar. However, there are fundamental differences in the physical mechanisms of scattering involved. Essentially the scattering of X-rays is by an electrical mechanism involving the density of the electrons in the scatterer. Scattering is weak for light atoms and strong for heavy atoms. Also, the electrons are distributed over the whole atom, the dimensions of which are not small compared with the wavelength of the radiation being scattered. This leads to a dependence of the magnitude of the scattering on the angle through which scattering occurs, expressed as the form factor. This quantity is in fact the Fourier transform of the spatial distribution of the density of the scattering charges (electrons).

For neutrons, scattering is by two basic mechanisms. One is the scattering of neutrons by nuclei. In this case the wavelength of the thermal neutrons is much larger (by a factor of about 10^4) than the nuclear diameter, causing the nuclear scattering to be isotropic. The amount of scattering is expressed quantitatively as the nuclear scattering amplitude b. This factor does not bear any simple relationship to the nuclear charge (atomic number) or mass. Light or heavy atoms may have similar values for b. Neighbouring elements or different isomers of the same element may have quite different values. Some nuclei have negative values of b, corresponding to a phase reversal of the neutron de Broglie wave on scattering. At present there is no full theory which accounts for how b varies from nucleus to nucleus. Since nuclear scattering takes no account of the magnetism of the neutron, the magnitude of the scattering is completely independent of the direction of the magnetic moments of the neutrons. Incident neutrons may also be captured by nuclei. The tendency for this to occur increases when certain resonance conditions involving nuclear energy level differences are approached.

The other scattering mechanism is magnetic scattering. When a neutron travels through the magnetic field caused by extra-nuclear electrons it is scattered by the interaction with its own magnetic moment. Because the atomic magnetic moment is usually spread out over distances comparable with the de Broglie wavelength of the neutrons the scattering depends on scattering through a magnetic form factor. This is the Fourier transform of the spatial distribution of the magnetic moment. The strength of the magnetic scattering depends on the magnetic moment of the scatterer, and the scattering depends on the directional relationship between the moment directions of the scatterer and the neutron.

Incident neutrons from a reactor will generally be unpolarized but it is possible to control their moment direction, producing polarized neutrons. There are many advantages in using polarized neutrons in magnetic work but there are additional experimental complications in achieving this.

For examining the magnetism of materials on the atomic scale, observations on the scattering of neutrons form a very useful tool.

5.2 Sources of neutrons

Neutron scattering experiments use neutrons from either thermal neutron reactors or from particle accelerators. The general layout is shown in

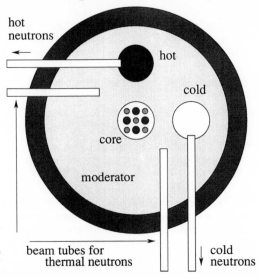

Figure 5.1 Schematic layout of thermal fission reaction, showing position of hot and cold sources and the beam tubes for hot, cold and thermal neutrons.

Figure 5.1 for a fission reactor and in Figure 5.2 for a particle accelerator. In a thermal fission reactor, slow neutrons are captured by ^{235}U. The uranium atom is caused to divide by fission, producing other energetic neutrons. Fast neutrons are not strongly absorbed and to sustain a chain reaction they must be slowed down by collision with the atoms of a moderator. This might be hydrogen or deuterium atoms in light (H_2O) or heavy (D_2O) water or the carbon atoms of graphite. When the geometry of the reactor is correct there is a self-sustaining equilibrium reaction. A relatively small excess of neutrons is allowed to escape through holes in the side of the reactor to be used for neutron beam experiments.

The sources using an accelerator are called Spallation Neutron Sources (SNS). Pulses of energetic protons are made to fall on a target of a heavy element (usually uranium) and neutrons are emitted. Because of the way the protons are accelerated to high energies, the neutrons come out in pulses. The usual method of use is to allow the full spectrum of available neutron wavelengths to fall as incident signals on the experimental specimens and then to sort out the emergent signals coming from the detectors under sophisticated computer control. Once the beam of neutrons has been produced the general principles involved in scattering and diffraction are the same as for work with fission reactors. High flux reactors produce about 2×10^{15} neutrons $\text{cm}^{-2}\,\text{s}^{-1}$, while medium flux reactors (the lower limit for useful neutron beam work) give about 10^{14} neutrons $\text{cm}^{-2}\,\text{s}^{-1}$.

The schematic arrangement of beam holes in a research reactor is shown in Figure 5.1.

The thermal neutrons have a broad energy range, giving a spectrum of

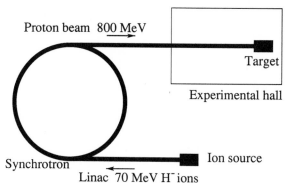

Figure 5.2 Schematic layout of spallation neutron source. The diameter of the synchrotron ring is of the order of 100 metres.

wavelengths similar to that in Figure 5.3. When a single wavelength is required it must be selected from this continuous spectrum of wavelengths, giving a relatively weak source of monochromatic neutrons.

It is possible to change the numerical distribution with wavelength of the neutrons by having a scattering body enclosed within the moderator that is maintained at a different temperature from the main body of the moderator. This is so positioned (Fig. 5.1) as to emit neutrons having a different wavelength distribution down a particular beam tube. Cold sources, with liquid hydrogen or liquid deuterium held at about 20 K can give very useful

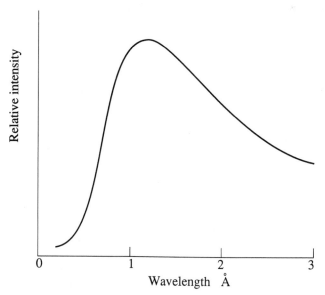

Figure 5.3 Wavelength distribution of thermal neutrons.

gains in flux for wavelengths greater than 1 nm (10 Å). Some scattering material containing a light element such as graphite or BeO held at about 2000 K can give increased fluxes for wavelengths under 0·1 nm (1 Å).

5.3 Powder diffraction

A typical experimental arrangement for powder diffraction is shown in Figure 5.4. It is the same arrangement as is used in X-ray powder diffraction but it is on a much larger scale. Neutron spectrometers normally have an operating circle having a radius of 1 metre or more. Neutron sources are much weaker than X-ray sources and since they are in no sense portable, the experiment must be taken to where the source is. Methods for detecting scattered neutrons are relatively cumbersome. Neutron counters are used and usually data must be collected over relatively long periods in order to provide acceptable counting statistics. Specimens must be relatively large, often occupying a volume of several cubic centimetres.

That the best possible use may be made of expensive neutron sources, experiments are usually made to run automatically under computer control, for 24 hours a day and 7 days a week. With the best conditions using a bank of position-sensitive detectors that cover a wide angular range without moving, a useful single diffraction scan can be completed in ten to thirty minutes.

5.3.1 Neutron detectors

Particle detectors usually depend for their operation on the ionization produced when the atomic particle being detected passes through matter. Because they are uncharged, neutrons are non-ionizing. They must therefore be detected by means of a secondary nuclear reaction where charged particles are produced and then detected by conventional gas ionization or solid-state scintillation techniques.

Reactions used are either (n,p) or (n,α) types, including the following:

$$^{10}B \ (n,\alpha) \ ^7Li$$
$$^3He \ (n,p) \ ^3H$$
$$^6Li \ (n,\alpha) \ ^3H$$

There must be high sensitivity for thermal neutrons and the lowest possible sensitivity for the γ-rays or fast neutrons, that are present as background near a nuclear reactor. Also, it is important in neutron diffraction that the position of the detection shall be sharply defined; that the dead time of the counter shall be a minimum; and that the electrical signal produced by the counter shall be as close as possible in time to the time of arrival of the neutron. Gas counters filled to a pressure of 1–2 bar with boron trifluoride enriched to about 95 per cent of the ^{10}B isotope are commonly used. For ordinary neutron diffraction purposes the counter is placed end-on to the incident neutrons, for maximum efficiency and surrounded by heavy shielding.

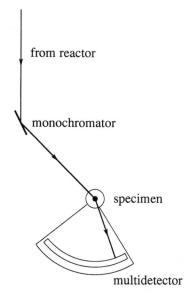

Figure 5.4 Plan of neutron powder diffractometer.

5.3.2 Single detectors

The traditional method of detecting scattered neutrons is for a single counter to be mounted on a carriage and moved round a circular track with the scattering specimen as centre. The entrance aperture of the counter always points towards the sample. The counter being surrounded by shielding ensures that the wanted signal entering through the aperture predominates over the unwanted background.

5.3.3 Photographic detection of neutrons

Neutrons do not directly influence photographic emulsions, because they produce no ionization directly. However, if neutrons are allowed to fall on a surface coated with a material containing atoms which capture neutrons with the emission of ionizing radiation and this surface is placed against a surface containing a scintillator which is in turn placed against a photographic emulsion, a photographic record of the arrival of neutrons can be obtained. This method is not used much for recording neutron diffraction patterns but it is used very extensively to produce shadow pictures for aligning experimental samples in the correct positions in incident neutron beams. Polaroid monochrome photographic paper is used and exposure times are about ten seconds.

5.3.4 Multidetectors

To improve the efficiency of the collection of diffraction data when using powdered or polycrystalline samples multidetectors have been developed.

These consist of many elements placed side by side inside a common gas space. Typically there are 400 cells at a spacing corresponding to five points per degree (80° in 2θ altogether) over a circle of radius 1·5 m. All count simultaneously. By displacing the array through a small angle more points per degree can be scanned.

Such techniques are being used more and more widely, since there is better use of the available neutrons. A single counter being moved round to measure at one position at a time loses all the data for the angles at which it is not placed and is very inefficient.

5.3.5 Monochromators

Since the thermal neutrons emerging from the reactor possess a range of energies, neutrons having a single wavelength to be used for diffraction must be selected by using a monochromator such as that shown in Figure 5.4. This is usually a single crystal of some suitable material located at the end of the exit hole from the reactor and set at such an angle that the neutrons leaving the monochromator and falling on the experimental specimen have the desired wavelength. Different materials are usually chosen for different wavelengths because in that way the available flux of neutrons can be optimized.

In a typical powder diffraction spectrometer the 002 reflection from pyrolytic graphite is used to get a wavelength of 0·252 nm (2·52 Å) while the 311 reflection from a single crystal of germanium is used for a wavelength of 0·128 nm (1·28 Å). Curved crystal monochromators give a focusing effect and improve the available intensity.

5.4 Inelastic neutron scattering

Where there is inelastic neutron scattering in crystals the incident neutrons give up part of their energy to (or receive energy from) the atoms of the crystal. The energy spectrum of lattice vibrations (atomic and magnetic) may be investigated. An important measurement is to establish the dispersion law for the elementary excitations of the magnetic crystal. These are for the phonons (atomic) and the magnons (magnetic). Magnons are also called spin waves. The energy distribution of the neutrons scattered coherently in any given direction with the emission or absorption of a single quantum of atomic or magnetic excitation contains maxima corresponding to simultaneous satisfaction of the quantum conditions of momentum and energy transfer. Scanning the energy of the scattered neutrons allows the maxima to be recognized.

If E_1 and E_2 are the initial and final neutron energies and ε is the energy of the crystal quantum then

$$E_1 - E_2 = \pm\varepsilon_k \qquad (5.1)$$

The positive value of ε_k corresponds to energy loss by the neutron (phonon or magnon creation). At the same time the momentum equation is

$$p_1 - p_2 + G = \pm k \tag{5.2}$$

where p_1 and p_2 are the initial and final neutron momentum (vectors), G is a reciprocal lattice vector and k is the wave vector of the crystal excitation. These two equations may be combined to give

$$(h/4\pi m)(p_1^2 - p_2^2) = \pm \varepsilon_k \tag{5.3}$$

The reciprocal lattice vector G represents the elastic (Bragg) scattering situation, illustrated in Figure 5.5.

Taking the reciprocal lattice point as origin it is possible to trace out variations in crystal momentum in chosen directions in reciprocal space. At any chosen value of the scattering angle the spectrometer is set to receive scattered neutrons in this direction. Performing an energy analysis of the neutrons received then shows the neutron energy at which the equations are satisfied, leading to information on the quantum energy of the scattering atoms. What is required for this experiment is a triple-axis spectrometer (Fig. 5.6). The axes involved, going outwards from the reactor, are:

(a) Axis 1. Rotation of monochromator crystal, to define the wavelength of the neutrons incident on the specimen and therefore p_1.

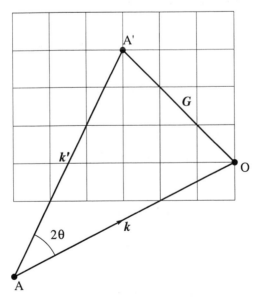

Figure 5.5 The Ewald construction in reciprocal space. k is the incident vector, k' is the scattered vector and G is the reciprocal lattice vector for scattering. θ is the Bragg angle.

    (b) Axis 2. Rotation of the experimental crystal to set up the emergent neutron wavelength and direction (and therefore p_2). At the Bragg condition the magnitudes of p_1 and p_2 are equal but their directions differ.

    (c) Axis 3. Rotation of an analysing crystal. This measures the wavelength of the scattered neutrons and therefore their energy.

What has been discussed here is the condition of constant $q\ (=p_1-p_2)$, with p_1 fixed, and variable energy E.

Depending on the particular quantities being measured and on the properties of the crystal under examination other types of scan may be used.

The variants are:

    (a) Fix either p_1 or p_2 (initial *or* final neutron momentum), fix q (where q is the crystal momentum $q = (p_1-p_2)$) and vary E, looking for maximum count at the optimum neutron energy.

    (b) Fix E and vary q.

Figure 5.7 illustrates the results obtained, using constant–q scans.

In actual experiments the instrument operates under computer control. The initial parameters such as the crystal parameters, the mode of operation, the fixed value of p_1 or p_2 and the range of scans required are supplied to the computer, which calculates the angular settings of the various axes of the spectrometer. It then controls the signals fed to a series of stepping motors associated with the angular movements so as to set the instrument to the required angle. The neutron count, which corresponds to

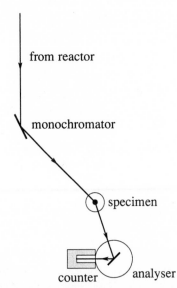

from reactor

monochromator

specimen

counter   analyser

Figure 5.6 Plan of three-circle inelastic neutron spectrometer.

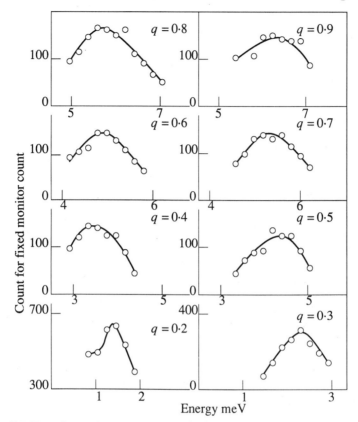

Figure 5.7 Experimental constant–q graphs for inelastic neutron scattering from dysprosium.

a preset value of the incident neutron count, is then collected. This is recorded in the computer memory and may be printed out numerically and graphically. Many scans can be programmed to run one after the other under automatic control from the computer. Each point on a scan might take up to 10 minutes to collect and one scan might contain about 20 points.

On such a triple axis spectrometer the various moving parts are usually supported on air pads which when they are energized from a compressed air supply may be moved around a very flat marble floor by the stepping motors, with very low friction. When the correct position has been found the computer cuts off the air supply to the individual feet, fixing them firmly in position. Figure 5.8 shows a magnon dispersion curve for a single crystal of ferromagnetic dysprosium measured in this way.

Since the wavelength and direction (with respect to the crystal) of the incident neutrons reaching the experimental sample are known, the incident wave vector k_i is defined. Similarly, the final wave vector k_f is known from the emergent direction and wavelength.

The change in wave vector (and thus the change in momentum Δp) is

$$(k_i - k_f) = 2\pi\tau \pm q \tag{5.4}$$

where $2\pi\tau$ is a reciprocal lattice vector determined by the crystallography.

Similarly the change in energy of the neutrons between initial and final states is

$$(E_i - E_f) = k_i^2(h^2/8\pi^2 m) - k_f^2(h^2/8\pi^2 m) \tag{5.5}$$

$$= \pm \omega(q)(h/2\pi)$$

The neutron is giving up or taking up energy and momentum in its interaction with a magnon in the sample, so q and $\omega(q)$ are respectively the wave vector and the energy of the magnon.

This experiment can be carried out only in regions of the reciprocal lattice where there are no spurious contributions from Bragg scattering. Also, the conditions must be such that the magnetic form factor for scattering is relatively large. This is for low values of $(\sin\theta/\lambda)$, where θ is the Bragg angle for the scattering.

Generally the choice is made at the outset of the experiment to look for conditions of magnon creation $(k_i > k_f)$ or of magnon annihilation $(k_f > k_i)$.

In the experiment the various angles are adjusted and the signal reaching the final counter is observed. In practice the procedure is simplified in order to keep the management of the data within reasonable limits. Either constant–q or constant–E scans are carried out.

In the constant–q technique the final neutron intensity is measured in steps. The spectrometer is so adjusted that for each step the value of q in Equation (5.9) remains unchanged. The magnon energy $\omega(q)$ varies. Counter output is plotted against $\omega(q)$ and maxima occur only for those energies corresponding to the intercept of the dispersion curve with the line for the value of q chosen. Scans are repeated for different values of the wave vector q and the course of the dispersion curve is given by the trace of the intensity peaks.

The constant–E method is exactly analogous to this. The two methods trace out respectively vertical and horizontal scans to fix the (ω, q) dispersion curve.

Which of these two methods is chosen depends on the exact shape of the dispersion curve being examined, in which region of the curve, on the characteristics of the spectrometer and on the quality of the crystal being examined.

Problems often arise in separating out those (ω, q) curves that are due to magnons and those that are due to phonons. In the end, the only certain distinction is obtained by using polarization analysis in the experiment. Magnons are sensitive to neutron polarization and phonons are not.

5.4.1 Results of magnon dispersion experiments with neutrons

Experiments have now been carried out on many magnetic materials, of different classes. Exchange integrals have been determined experimentally. However, this is difficult when the magnon can only be detected for a small range of the wave vector.

Iron has an isotropic dispersion curve but its shape deviates from what would be expected for a simple Heisenberg ferromagnet. Stiffness constants D have been determined for iron and nickel but the values are inconsistent with estimates made by other experiments.

5.5 The polarization of neutron beams

With magnetic materials, the scattering process depends on the relative moment directions of the neutrons and the scatterer. While the scattering of an unpolarized beam of randomly oriented neutrons gives useful information about the magnetism of the scatterer, very much more can be obtained with polarized neutrons.

5.5.1 Production of polarized beams by selective Bragg reflection

In Section 5.1 it was described how, when an incident neutron interacts with an atom possessing a magnetic moment two processes occur simultaneously, nuclear scattering and magnetic scattering. The intensity of nuclear scattering is angle-independent and magnetic scattering is subject to an angle-dependent form factor. The ratio of the magnitudes of the nuclear and magnetic components differs for different Bragg peaks and the scattering amplitudes of the two components sometimes differ in sign.

The spin axis of the neutrons can be defined with respect to the direction of a magnetic field applied to the scatterer, so that we may think of parallel (up) and anti-parallel (down) spin components.

If we can arrange for the nuclear and the up-spin magnetic components of one particular Bragg peak of a chosen scatterer to compensate exactly and to cancel out, what remains will be wholly of one spin state and will be uniquely polarized.

Such a condition is very closely achieved with the (111) reflection from a single crystal of the Heusler alloy Cu_2MnAl or with the (111) reflection from a face-centred cubic cobalt–iron alloy single crystal containing 8 per cent of iron. Polarization efficiencies greater than 99 per cent are obtained in this way and the method is commonly used, but the ensuing polarized beam is relatively weak.

5.5.2 Production of polarized beams using supermirrors

Neutrons may be reflected albeit with small angular deflections, by total reflection at the surface of a magnetized solid mirror. The reflection depends on the spin state of the neutrons. By careful selection of the relative magnitudes of nuclear and magnetic components by choice of the mirror material it is possible to obtain the reflection of only one of the spin states. In this simple case high polarization efficiency is obtained, but poor beam intensity.

The effectiveness of this device has been improved by the development of multilayer mirrors, or supermirrors. The solid surface is coated with a series of layers of alternating reflectivity, so creating an artificial two-dimensional crystal. Careful choice of the layer spacing optimizes the polarization efficiency and the beam strength. Such a supermirror may use about 75 alternating layers of silver and iron and 99 per cent polarization efficiency is achieved.

5.5.3 Production of polarized beams using polarizing transmission filters

The use of these devices is still in its infancy. Ideally they have a great advantage in that they polarize the neutron beam without any fundamental effect on the trajectory of the neutrons or on the beam energy. Such an ideal filter would be opaque to one neutron spin state and fully transparent to the other.

What is needed is a filter material having a large spin-dependent cross section for neutrons having low energy, which is itself capable of being aligned preferentially. Polarized hydrogen has been used in nuclear physics for polarizing high energy neutrons. However, for thermal neutrons the process is less attractive and achieving an acceptable alignment of the hydrogen atoms is difficult.

Polarized ^{3}He is a very promising filter material but so far it has not been used in a working neutron polarizer. The absorption of ^{3}He for neutrons down to low energies is very large and it is spin-independent in an ideal way. Thus it is opaque for one neutron spin state and transparent for the other. Experiments are in progress to try to design an effective and economic way of polarizing the helium. One method is to apply a 14 T field to the paramagnetic solid phase of ^{3}He (at high pressure and very low temperature). Another method is to polarize ^{3}He in the gas phase with polarized laser light. The use of ^{3}He filters is highly promising and is likely to be in common use soon.

The powder diffraction patterns for a ferromagnetic material, obtained with and without the magnetic component of scattering by means of polarization analysis are clearly distinguished and the magnetic scattering can be measured reliably.

5.6 Engineering applications of neutron scattering

Neutron scattering is the most powerful single technique for examining the details of magnetism in solid materials on the atomic scale and there are ever growing applications.

Recently there have been applications of neutron diffraction to mechanical and civil engineering. For many years X-ray diffraction has been used to investigate stress and strain distributions in engineering components and at interfaces between components. Diffraction experiments allow lattice parameters to be measured as a function of position across a sample and comparison of the results with an unstressed sample of the same material allows a stress field to be evaluated. However, because X-rays are strongly absorbed in solids, only the surfaces of the specimens contribute to the results and it is never clear to what extent the surface represents the interior.

By contrast, since neutrons can fairly easily pass right through solid samples the results obtained from similar observations using neutrons are definitely representative of the insides of bulk samples. By careful collimation of incident and emergent neutrons the position of the scattering element inside a solid can be accurately defined and a three-dimensional stress map can be obtained. This technique is new and it is highly promising.

5.7 Magnetic excitations and spin waves

In Chapters 2 and 3 we assumed that the thermal average of the magnetic moment at a given atomic site in a crystal is well defined and is not subject to fluctuations. Essentially we assumed that we deal with a static state, even though it is the average of a thermal excitation of various higher energy states. However, the actual situation is a dynamic one.

Let us consider first a system of spins on identical lattice sites coupled ferromagnetically by exchange interaction, in perfect alignment at zero temperature. We can define an axis of quantization with reference to the direction of an insignificantly small applied magnetic field. Now let the temperature be raised slightly, providing enough thermal energy for one spin in the system to be reversed. Because of the coupling between this reversed spin and its neighbours, the neighbours will be influenced and a wave of reversed spin will propagate through the crystal, its form being controlled by the strength and form of the exchange interactions and by the fundamental stiffness of the spins on the lattice. This is called a spin wave, or magnon. It is analogous to a phonon, which is the propagation of elastic waves in the lattice under the influence of the cohesive forces between the atoms. Both spin waves (magnons) and lattice waves (phonons) can be treated as though they are quasi-particles, obeying Bose-Einstein statistics. The spin wave model really applies to where the deviations from the ideally aligned lattice are not too great; that is, at temperatures fairly low compared with the Curie temperature. In general the wavelengths involved are quite long, extending over many unit cells.

A closely similar situation occurs at domain boundaries in ferromagnets. This is described in Chapter 8 and shown diagrammatically in Figure 8.3, where the adjustment of the direction of magnetization at a boundary is constrained to take place gradually between the atoms by the exchange forces which tend to resist such change.

The theoretical treatment of spin waves depends on the class of magnetic solid being considered. The extremes are an ionic, localized material on the one hand and a metal in which the magnetism is delocalized on the other hand. The predictions of the theory are roughly similar for the different cases, where there are small deviations from the ground state that is at the absolute zero of temperature.

We find that the energy of the spin wave (magnon)

$$E = h\nu = (h/2\pi)\omega$$

is related to its wave number q by

$$E = Dq^2 + E_0 \tag{5.6}$$

The wave number q is a measure of the momentum p of the magnon, since

$$p = hk = (h/2\pi)q$$

$$k = (2\pi/\lambda)$$

where λ is the wavelength of the magnon.

$$q = (1/\lambda)$$

Small values of q correspond to long wavelengths.

Equation (5.4) emphasizes the similarity with the case for phonons. D has the nature of a stiffness constant and it is so called for magnons as well as phonons.

D is controlled by the strength of the interactions that stabilize the magnetically ordered state, since

$$D \text{ is proportional to } SJ_e a^2 \tag{5.7}$$

where S is the local spin, J_e is the effective exchange constant and a is the lattice parameter.

E_0 is the static energy of the spin in the total magnetic field which acts, $(B_0)_T$.

This is made up of any applied field compounded with the anisotropy field.

$$E_0 \text{ is proportional to } g\,\mu_B(B_0)_T \tag{5.8}$$

Equation (5.4) is valid when only magnons of long wavelength are excited. Deviations may be treated phenomenologically by a power series expansion

$$E = Dq^2(1 - \beta q^2 + \gamma q^4 + \ldots) + E_0 \tag{5.9}$$

Simple application of this theory leads to the expectation that at low temperatures the spontaneous magnetization depends on temperature according to

$$\sigma_{0,T}/\sigma_{0,0} = (1 - A(T/T_C)^{3/2}) \tag{5.10}$$

where A is a constant determined by the fundamental interactions.

This is first-order theory and experiment shows deviations, but it forms the basis of starting to understand the experimental behaviour observed. The most direct and most powerful experimental approach is by using inelastic neutron scattering. Neutrons with energies in the thermal range exchange energy and momentum with magnons and relatively simple techniques of neutron detection enable the main parameters to be measured directly. Figure 5.8 gives an example of a dispersion curve for ferromagnetic dysprosium.

Measuring the dispersion curve directly gives information about exchange interactions and about fundamental anisotropy behaviour.

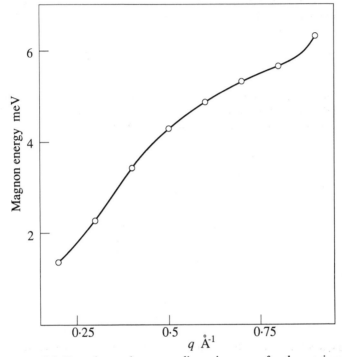

Figure 5.8 Experimental magnon dispersion curve for dysprosium.

5.8 Brillouin zones in metals

As background to the application of the results of inelastic neutron scattering to the behaviour of magnons in magnetic metals, here we give an elementary and brief resumé of Brillouin zone theory.

5.8.1 Interaction between conduction electrons and the lattice periodicity

The conduction electrons in a metal act as though they are nearly free, being constrained only by the bounds of the metal sample. They have a range of energy from zero up to the Fermi energy. The varying energies correspond to a continuum of wavelengths for the travelling waves which represent the electrons. Singularities occur when the electron wavelengths relate to the lattice periodicity and satisfy the Bragg diffraction condition. When this occurs Bragg reflection takes place and for the particular wavelength the wave does not transmit. The three-dimensional locus of where this occurs, drawn in reciprocal space, is called the Brillouin zone boundary.

The shape of the Brillouin zone differs for different crystal structures. Figure 5.9 shows the first Brillouin zone for a face-centred cubic structure. In a cubic structure of lattice parameter a the first zone boundary along a cube edge direction is where

$$k = \pm (\pi/a) \text{ and}$$

$$q = \pm (1/2a)$$

How the energy of electrons varies with k (or q) in selected directions across a Brillouin zone (particularly the first) is of considerable interest since this is one of the factors which determine the main physical properties

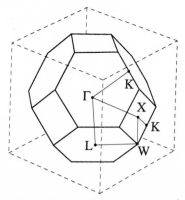

Figure 5.9 First Brillouin zone for a face-centred cubic structure.

of the solid. An example of this (E,k) relationship for the first Brillouin zone of aluminium is illustrated in Figure 5.10. It should be noted that the scale of energies that occurs in this context is relatively large, being of the order of electron volts for the full range.

Similarly, the form of the (energy, momentum) relationships for the small excitations that we call magnons is of great interest in trying to understand the interactions which control them. Here the range of energies is much smaller, usually of the order of milli-electron volts (meV).

5.9 Spin wave resonance

As might be expected, low energy magnon excitations can be detected by

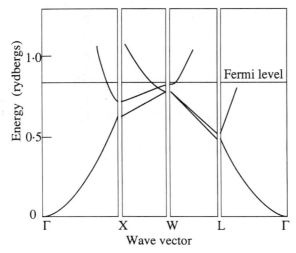

Figure 5.10 Calculated E, k graphs for the first zone in aluminium (after Segall, 1961, *Phys. Rev.*, **124**, 1797).

microwave resonance methods. The resonant frequency is v in the equation

$$hv = g\mu_B(B_0 - \mu_0 M) + Dk^2 \tag{5.11}$$

B_0 is an external DC magnetic field applied normal to the plane of a thin film sample and M is its magnetization. k is an experimental parameter related to the wave number of the spin wave. D is the same stiffness parameter that is observed in the neutron inelastic data.

Chapter 6 ⎯⎯⎯⎯⎯⎯⎯⎯

Antiferromagnetism, ferrimagnetism and non-collinear magnetic order

6.1 Antiferromagnetism

Antiferromagnetism is a state in which the atomic magnetic moments in a solid are ideally aligned as they are in a perfect ferromagnet, but the individual moments are arranged in a self-compensatory way so that there is no overall spontaneous magnetization.

As we have seen already, ferromagnetism occurs when there is a positive exchange interaction which may be described as a molecular field in the same direction as the local magnetization in the neighbourhood of a magnetic centre. The idea that the remaining non-ferromagnetic members of the first transition (3d) series of elements (Mn, Cr, V, Ti, Sc) might have negative interactions led to a theoretical study of the properties of antiferromagnetic systems. Néel (between 1932 and 1936) was the first to show that such a system has a critical temperature, now called the Néel temperature T_N, below which the atomic moments are arranged alternately parallel and antiparallel to a preferred direction. Above T_N the moments are disordered paramagnetically, as in a ferromagnet above the Curie temperature T_C. It is now known that the metals to which the first ideas were applied do not necessarily exhibit the simple antiferromagnetism envisaged. The first clear experimental confirmation of antiferromagnetism was obtained for non-metallic materials about 1950. Antiferromagnetism was found in metals about ten years later.

The simplest type of antiferromagnet is one in which the crystal may be divided into two sublattices, A and B, so that if the spins of one sublattice point one way, those of the other point the opposite way. The spins of nearest-neighbour atoms are always antiparallel to each other.

Simple cubic and body-centred cubic crystal structures may fit this requirement, but face-centred cubic structures may not. It is assumed that the interatomic interactions can be represented again by a molecular field, but with a coefficient opposite in sign to that for a Weiss ferromagnet. The model is illustrated in Figure 6.1.

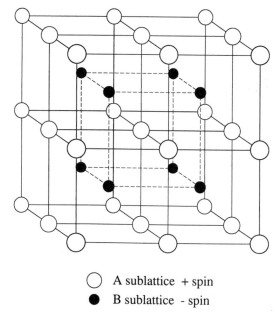

○ A sublattice + spin

● B sublattice − spin

Figure 6.1 Two-sublattice model of an antiferromagnet.

6.1.1 Magnetization of the sublattices

Let $\sigma_A = 1/2N_s\langle\mu_{J\uparrow}\rangle_A$ be the magnetization per unit mass of the A sublattice (half the total number of atoms), and similarly for σ_B and the B sublattice.

Taking first and second nearest neighbour interactions into account, the molecular fields q acting respectively on the atoms of the A and the B sublattices are

$$B_i^A = q_{AA}\sigma_A + q_{AB}\sigma_B \tag{6.1}$$

and

$$B_i^B = q_{BA}\sigma_A + q_{BB}\sigma_B \tag{6.2}$$

In the present case the two sublattices are equivalent, and

$q_{AB} = q_{BA} = -q_1$ (first neighbours), and

$q_{AA} = q_{BB} = -q_2$ (second neighbours).

q_1 and q_2 are both positive.

The magnetizations of the two sublattices may now be written down in a similar way to that for the ferromagnetic case in Chapter 2 (compare Equations (2.8) and (2.9)). Again we calculate the spontaneous magnetization, with no external field applied.

$$(\sigma_A)_T = 1/2N_sJg\mu_BF(J, y_A') \tag{6.3}$$

and

$$(\sigma_B)_T = 1/2 N_s J g \mu_B F(J, y'_B) \tag{6.4}$$

where

$$y'_A = J g \mu_B B_i^A / kT, \text{ and } y'_B = J g \mu_B B_i^B / kT$$

Since σ_A and σ_B have the same magnitude and opposite directions, we put

$$\sigma_A = -\sigma_B \text{ and } |\sigma_A| = \sigma_s$$

Then

$$\sigma_s = 1/2 N_s J g \mu_B F(J, y'_s)$$

where

$$y'_s = J g \mu_B \sigma_s (q_1 - q_2) / kT$$

Putting $q_1 - q_2 = q$ (equivalent to γ_m in Equation (2.9)) and $\sigma_0 = N_s J g \mu_B$ we see that the solution takes exactly the same form as the ferromagnetic case considered in Chapter 2. Each sublattice is expected to be spontaneously magnetized with a value depending on temperature, as shown in Figure 6.2. The overall magnetization is zero since the two sublattice magnetizations are always equal and opposite.

Sublattice magnetizations may be measured by neutron diffraction, from the intensity of the magnetic scattering of the neutrons. Observations made on ionic materials (MnF_2 is an example) have confirmed that the theory given above is essentially correct.

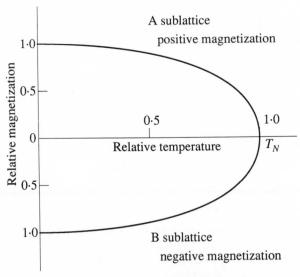

Figure 6.2 Spontaneous magnetization of the sublattices in a single antiferromagnet.

The Néel temperature T_N may be calculated as T_C was calculated in the ferromagnetic case, with γ_m replaced by $q = q_1 - q_2$.

$$T_N = (q_1 - q_2)1/2N_s g^2 \mu_B^2 J(J+1)/3k = 1/2(q_1 - q_2)C \tag{6.5}$$

6.1.2 Susceptibility above the Néel temperature

Here the magnetizations are again small and we can use the approximate form of the Brillouin function. For the magnetization of the two sublattices.

$$\sigma_A = 1/2N_s p_{eff}^2 (B_0 - q_2 \sigma_A - q_1 \sigma_B)/3kT \quad \text{and}$$
$$\sigma_B = 1/2N_s p_{eff}^2 (B_0 - q_1 \sigma_A - q_2 \sigma_B)/3kT$$

where, as in Chapter 2, $p_{eff}^2 = g^2 J(J+1)$.

Adding these two equations together,

$$3kT(\sigma_A + \sigma_B) = 1/2N_s p_{eff}^2 \mu_B^2 (2B_0 - (q_1 + q_2)(\sigma_A + \sigma_B)) \tag{6.6}$$

Thus the total mass susceptibility

$$\chi = (\sigma_A + \sigma_B)/B_0$$
$$= C/(T - \theta_p) \tag{6.7}$$

where $C = N_s p_{eff}^2 \mu_B^2/3k$ and

$$\theta_p = -1/2(q_1 + q_2)C$$

when $T = T_N$, $\chi = 1/q_1$

This is the same relationship as that found for an ionic ferromagnet above its Curie temperature, except that for the antiferromagnet the intercept of the Curie-Weiss relationship on the $1/\chi = 0$ axis is at a negative temperature.

The ratio θ_p/T_N depends on the relationship between the first and the second nearest neighbour interactions.

$$\theta_p/T_N = -(q_1 + q_2)/(q_1 - q_2) \tag{6.8}$$

θ_p and T_N are of opposite sign.

In this model the ratio is only unity if there is no molecular field due to interactions within the same sublattice. That is, when $q_2 = 0$ and also $q_{AA} = q_{BB} = 0$. From Equation (6.8) it would appear that θ_p/T_N would become very large if the second neighbour coefficient q_2 was nearly equal to q_1, their difference tending to zero. In fact this is not the case, for if the ratio q_2/q_1 exceeds a certain value it is energetically more favourable to have a different magnetic structure in which all the spins in the respective sublattices cease to be parallel to each other. A new arrangement of sublattices forms. How the sublattices are arranged in a given antiferromagnetic material can be found from neutron diffraction experiments.

A given crystal structure may be made up of more than two magnetic sublattices. A face-centred cubic lattice is made up of four simple cubic sublattices. The twelve nearest neighbours of one atom are distributed equally among the three other sublattices. The six second nearest neighbours belong to the same sublattice as the central atom. The treatment is now more complicated but the general results are similar to the two-sublattice case. However, the ratio θ_p/T_N is differently related to q_1 and q_2.

6.1.3 Susceptibility below the Néel temperature

In calculating the susceptibility below T_N it is important to take into account the direction of the applied field with respect to the direction of the spins. There are major differences according to whether the field is perpendicular to the spins or parallel. In a polycrystalline material, the relative orientation will lie between these limits. The spins of all the various sublattices in one domain point parallel to or antiparallel to the same direction and this direction will vary from one domain to another.

We may take the average of the effects throughout the sample of the perpendicular and the parallel components of the field by writing

$$\chi = 2/3\chi_{perp} + 1/3\chi_{par} \tag{6.9}$$

What happens when perpendicular and parallel fields are applied to such an antiferromagnet can be seen qualitatively from Figure 6.3. In the perpendicular case, application of a field increases the magnetization in the field direction equally for both kinds of spin. Representing the effect of increasing temperature by showing an increasing divergence of spins, we expect the induced magnetization and thus the perpendicular susceptibility to be the same at all temperatures from $T = 0$ to $T = T_N$. In the parallel direction at $T = 0$ we expect a small field to have no effect on the spins and the parallel susceptibility to be zero. When the temperature and thus the divergence increases there is more out-of-line moment which may be pulled into line by the field. That is, we expect a parallel susceptibility which increases from $\chi_{par} = 0$ at $T = 0$ until it reaches the paramagnetic value at $T = T_N$. We would also expect that a sufficiently strong field would be capable of reversing antiparallel spins and would convert the

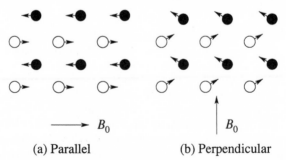

(a) Parallel   (b) Perpendicular

Figure 6.3 Application of parallel and perpendicular fields to a simple antiferromagnet.

antiferromagnetic state into one with a nearly saturated ferromagnetic moment.

6.1.4 Perpendicular susceptibility

The effect of the field is to deflect the magnetic moments σ_A and σ_B of both sublattices through a small angle θ towards the direction of the field (Fig. 6.3). It is assumed that the magnitudes of σ_A and σ_B remain unchanged. The angle of deflection θ is that angle at which the torques from the various fields acting on a given spin balance out. The A sublattice is acted upon by

(a) the applied field B_0, exerting a torque $B_0 \cos \theta$ which is clockwise in the diagram,
(b) the first neighbour molecular field $q_1\sigma_B$, exerting a torque of $q_1\sigma_B \sin 2\theta$ (anticlockwise), and
(c) the second neighbour molecular field $q_2\sigma_A$, exerting no torque since it always has the same direction as σ_A.

For small θ, in equilibrium

$$B_0 = q_1\sigma_B 2\theta, \text{ or } \theta = 1/2 B_0/\sigma_s q_1$$

The magnetization induced in the direction of the field is $2\sigma_s\theta$, and the perpendicular susceptibility is given by

$$\chi_{perp} = 2\sigma_s\theta/B_0 = 1/q_1 \tag{6.10}$$

This is independent of temperature so long as the first molecular field coefficient q_1 is independent of temperature. It is equal to the value of the paramagnetic susceptibility at T_N.

6.1.5 Parallel susceptibility

In calculating the parallel susceptibility we need to know the changes $\Delta\sigma_A$ and $\Delta\sigma_B$ produced in the magnetization of each sublattice when the field (assumed to be in the direction of σ_A and antiparallel to σ_B) changes from zero to B_0. Then

$$\chi_{par} = (\Delta\sigma_A + \Delta\sigma_B)/B_0$$

Again we write (similarly to Equations (6.3) and (6.4))

$$\sigma_A = 1/2 N_s Jg \mu_B F(J, y_A'') \tag{6.11}$$

and

$$\sigma_B = 1/2 N_s Jg \mu_B F(J, y_B'') \tag{6.12}$$

where

$$y_A'' = Jg\mu_B(B_0 - q_1\sigma_B - q_2\sigma_A)/kT$$

$-y_B'' = Jg\mu_B(B_0 - q_1\sigma_A - q_2\sigma_B)/kT$ and $F(J, y'')$ is the Brillouin function. As an approximation in the expression for y'' we write $\sigma_A = -\sigma_B$

$$y''_A = Jg\mu_B(\sigma(q_1 - q_2) + B_0)/kT \tag{6.13}$$

and

$$y''_B = Jg\mu_B(\sigma(q_1 - q_2) - B_0)/kT \tag{6.14}$$

Equations (6.13) and (6.14) may be written in the form of Equation (2.10).

$$\sigma_A/Jg\mu_B N_s = ATy'' - C \tag{6.15}$$

and

$$\sigma_B/Jg\mu_B N_s = ATy'' + C \tag{6.16}$$

where

$$A = k/(Jg\mu_B)^2 N_s(q_1 - q_2) \text{ and } C = B_0/Jg\mu_B N_s(q_1 - q_2)$$

The magnetization σ_A of the A sublattice is given by the simultaneous solution of Equations (6.11) and (6.15), or Equations (6.12) and (6.16) for σ_B (Fig. 6.4). $\Delta\sigma_A$ is the change in σ_A when B_0 is increased from zero, and likewise for $\Delta\sigma_B$.

$\Delta\sigma_A$ is given by $B_0/(q_1 - q_2)$ times the gradient of the Brillouin function evaluated at the equilibrium value of y'' when $B_0 = 0$. $\Delta\sigma_B$ has the same value as $\Delta\sigma_A$, since it corresponds to a decrease in magnetization in the direction opposite to that of the field. The parallel susceptibility

$$\chi_{par} = (\Delta\sigma_A + \Delta\sigma_B)/B_0$$

is therefore approximately proportional to the gradient of the Brillouin function against y'', evaluated for $B_0 = 0$.

When the sublattice magnetization is saturated (at $T = 0$ and therefore at high values of y''), χ_{par} is zero. With increasing temperature χ_{par} rises

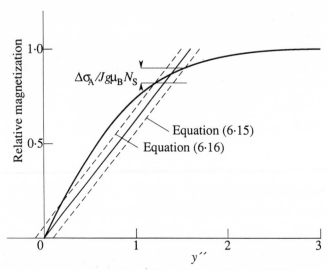

Figure 6.4 Solution of Equations (6.15) and (6.16).

until it reaches the value for the paramagnetic state ($y'' \rightarrow 0$) at $T = T_N$. Also at the Néel temperature, $\chi_{par} = \chi_{perp}$. The susceptibility of a randomly oriented polycrystalline sample is now (see Equation (6.9)).

$$\chi = 2/3\chi_{perp} + 1/3\chi_{par}$$

The expected variation with temperature of the susceptibility of a simple ionic antiferromagnet is shown in Figure 6.5. We have been discussing a model in which the ions may be distributed between two magnetic sublattices. The numerical details of the calculation are different for more sublattices but the principal feature of the result, the expected maximum of the susceptibility at T_N, remains. This is usually found experimentally for ionic antiferromagnets, as Figure 6.6 illustrates.

6.1.6 Effect of crystal anisotropy

The case considered so far is one in which the influence of the crystal structure on the direction of the atomic magnetic moments has been neglected. The dominant force aligning the spins was assumed to be the isotropic exchange interaction. More usually we need to take into account a crystal anistropy energy which determines the orientation of the magnetic moments with respect to the crystal directions. The direction of the magnetic moments when the energy is lowest is called an easy direction. The crystal anistropy energy $\Phi(\theta)$ is a function of the angular displacement θ of the moments from this direction. In weak fields the direction of the

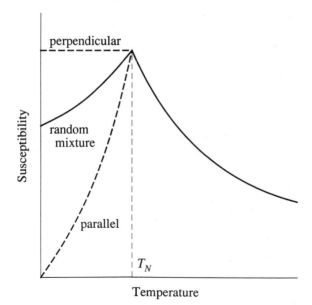

Figure 6.5 Calculated susceptibility of a simple ionic antiferromagnetic single crystal in the parallel and perpendicular directions and for a random mixture of the two.

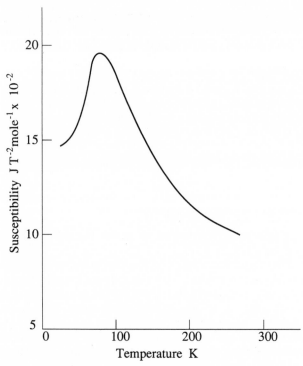

Figure 6.6 Measured susceptibility of antiferromagnetic FeF_2. The Néel temperature is at 79 K (after Bizette, 1951, *J. Physique*, **12**, 161).

moments is defined by the easy direction and the case that we have been considering holds where the applied field may be resolved into perpendicular and parallel components. The magnetic energy E_m is then given by

$$E_m = 1/2\chi_{perp}(B_0)^2_{perp} - 1/2\chi_{par}(B_0)^2_{par} \qquad (6.17)$$

In stronger fields the moments may be deflected away from the easy direction and the total energy must include the anisotropy energy. The total energy is

$$E = -1/2\chi_{perp}(B_0)^2_{perp} - 1/2\chi_{par}(B_0)^2_{par} + \Phi(\theta) \qquad (6.18)$$

The angle of deflection is that which minimizes the total energy, and the susceptibility is different from the undeflected value. Thus the susceptibility is expected to depend on the applied field at high field strengths in an ionic antiferromagnet at a temperature below T_N. This has been found experimentally.

6.1.7 Antiferromagnetism in metals

The antiferromagnetic properties described so far relate most closely to non-metals. The ions are well-separated and we are not much concerned with band properties. Many metals also are antiferromagnetic but their properties tend to be complicated by their electrons being in energy bands of appreciable width which tend to overlap. There is a wide variety of behaviour. Some metals have simple antiferromagnetic structures and their susceptibilities follow the Curie-Weiss law above T_N with a clear maximum at the Néel temperature. An example is given in Figure 6.7. Sometimes

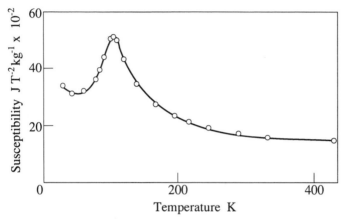

Figure 6.7 Susceptibility of the metallic antiferromagnet Pt_3Fe.

metals are antiferromagnetic and little if any effect on the susceptibility is seen at T_N. Metallic manganese and chromium are examples of this (Fig. 6.8). The simple ionic theory of the susceptibility cannot usually be applied to metallic antiferromagnets. Sometimes other, more complicated, forms of antiferromagnetism occur which involve non-collinear moments. Some of these are described later in this chapter.

6.2 Ferrimagnetism

A ferrimagnetic material is one in which the magnetic moments of the atoms on different sublattices oppose as in antiferromagnets; but the opposing moments are unequal and a spontaneous magnetization remains. This behaviour was first recognized in the technologically important group of materials called ferrites and it occurs most frequently in non-metals.

6.2.1 Structure of the spinel ferrites

Ferrites are semiconductors or insulators having the general chemical formula $XO . Y_2O_3$, the X cation usually being divalent and the Y cation trivalent. These substances possess the same structures as the mineral spinel. It consists of a close-packed face-centred cubic arrangement of the oxygen anions, the cations being distributed in the two kinds of interstitial site between them. The unit cell contains 32 anions and 24 cations

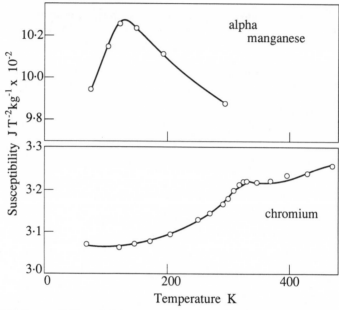

Figure 6.8 Susceptibility of alpha-manganese (after Kreissman and McGuire, 1955, *Phys. Rev.*, **98**, 936) and of chromium (after Lingelbach, 1958, *Z. Phys. Chem.* **14**, 1).

altogether, of both kinds X and Y. Eight cations on A sites are surrounded tetrahedrally by four oxygen ions and the remaining sixteen cations on B sites are surrounded octahedrally by six oxygen ions. In the structure that is called normal the divalent X cations occupy the tetrahedral A sites and the trivalent Y ions occupy the octahedral B sites. The structure called inverse occurs when half the Y ions occupy A sites, the remaining X and Y cations being randomly distributed among the octahedral B sites. These structures were found by X-ray and neutron diffraction experiments. Some ferrites, such as magnesium ferrite $MgO \cdot Fe_2O_3$, possess the inverse structure and some, such as zinc ferrite $ZnO \cdot Fe_2O_3$ have the normal structure.

The general properties of spinel ferrites were explained by the two-sublattice theory of (collinear) ferrimagnetism published by Néel in 1948.

Other materials in the same general class are the hexagonal ferrites (magnetoplumbites), such as barium ferrite $BaFe_{12}O_{19}$, and the ferrimagnetic garnets. A well-known example of the latter is yttrium iron garnet (also called YIG) $Y_3Fe_5O_{12}$ or $5Fe_2O_3 \cdot 3Y_2O_3$.

6.2.2 Two-sublattice theory of ferrimagnetism

The two sublattice theory of ferrimagnetism is really an extension of the one described already for a two sublattice antiferromagnet. The magnetizations of the two sublattices oppose each other but they are not equal.

The intrinsic magnetization per unit mass of the whole specimen is

$$\sigma = \lambda\sigma_1 - (1-\lambda)\sigma_2$$

where σ_1 and σ_2 are the respective magnetizations of the two sublattices and λ is a fraction between 0 and 1. When $\lambda = 1/2$ we have antiferromagnetism and when $\lambda = 1$ (or zero) we have ferromagnetism.

6.2.3 Susceptibility of the paramagnetic state above the Curie temperature

Above the Curie temperature T_C, y'' is small (see Section 6.1.2). The applied field B_0 induces a small moment σ which is in the same direction as B_0. Then sublattice magnetization σ_1 is in the same direction. σ_2 is in the opposite direction and thus opposes the field B_0.

The field acting on the first sublattice is

$$B_0 + q_1(1-\lambda)\sigma_2 + q_2\lambda\sigma_1$$

On the second sublattice a field

$$-B_0 + q_1\lambda\sigma_1 + q_2(1-\lambda)\sigma_2 \text{ acts.}$$

q_1 and q_2 are again the first and second neighbour molecular field coefficients.

We allow for the possibility of the two sublattices being made up of different kinds of ion (with different p_{eff}), and in the approximate form of the Brillouin function we write.

$$C = N_s p_{eff}^2 \mu_B^2 / 3k,$$

so that

$$\sigma_1 = [B_0 + q_1(1-\lambda)\sigma_2 + q_2\lambda\sigma_1]C_1/T \tag{6.19}$$

and

$$\sigma_2 = [-B_0 + q_1\lambda\sigma_1 + q_2(1-\lambda)\sigma_2]C_2/T \tag{6.20}$$

These equations may be solved for σ_1 and σ_2 and the reciprocal of the total susceptibility is

$$1/\chi = B_0/\sigma = B_0/(\lambda\sigma_1 - \{1-\lambda\}\sigma_2)$$

The solution may be written in the form

$$1/\chi = T/C + 1/\chi_0 + A/(T-\theta) \tag{6.21}$$

where C, χ_0, A and θ are constants which may be expressed in terms of λ, q_1, q_2, C_1 and C_2.

This relationship shows a hyperbolic dependence of $1/\chi$ on T, agreeing with what is often found experimentally in ferrimagnets (Fig. 1.10). It approaches a Curie-Weiss relationship at high temperatures, when the term $A/(T-\theta)$ becomes small.

The Curie temperature T_C (the highest temperature at which a spontaneous magnetic moment can exist) may be calculated in this theory by writing $1/\chi = 0$ and $T = T_C$ in Equation (6.21).

6.2.4 Magnetization below the Curie temperature

Néel applied the two-sublattice theory to calculate the magnetization of each sublattice below T_C, and therefore the total magnetization. Instead of using the approximate form of the Brillouin function in the expressions for σ_1 and σ_2 (Equations (6.19) and (6.20)) the full form was used. A numerical method of solution for σ_1 and σ_2 was followed, very similar to that described in Section 2.6.1 for the single sublattice ionic ferromagnet.

The way in which the total spontaneous magnetization

$$\sigma = \lambda\sigma_1 - (1-\lambda)\sigma_2$$

of the ferrimagnet varies with temperature depends markedly on the relative magnitudes of the molecular field coefficients and of the quantity parameter λ. Some of the results which Néel predicted are shown qualitatively in Figure 6.9.

All these forms of curve have now been observed experimentally, supporting Néel's theory in a remarkable way. Figure 6.10 shows the experimentally determined curve of spontaneous magnetization against temperature for manganese ferrite.

The unusual prediction, that in some cases the net magnetic moment goes through a so-called compensation point of zero magnitude and then changes its sign before finally vanishing at the Curie temperature, has been

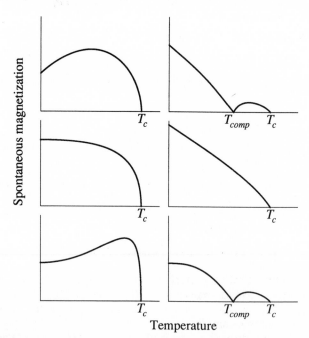

Figure 6.9 Calculated dependence of magnetization on temperature for different classes of two-sublattice ferrimagnet.

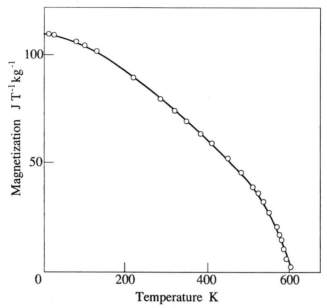

Figure 6.10 Experimental graph of magnetization against temperature for ferrimagnetic manganese ferrite $MnO . Fe_2O_3$.

observed experimentally as shown in Figure 6.11. Which sublattice dominates is not immediately obvious. Between the compensation temperatures and T_C the overall spontaneous magnetization increases with increasing temperature, it passes through a maximum and then it finally approaches zero again at T_C.

6.2.5 Saturation magnetic moment of spinel ferrites

When it is known which magnetic ions occupy which kind of site within the crystal structure the saturation moment may be calculated very simply. In some cases the structure is neither inverse nor normal but is a mixed structure lying between the two. The occupation parameters for the A and B sites can be measured by neutron diffraction experiments. Characteristics of several kinds of cation are given in Table 6.1. Calculated and experimental values of the saturation magnetic moment of a number of spinel ferrites are given in Table 6.2. There is generally quite good agreement between experiment and theory.

Zinc ferrite $ZnO . Fe_2O_3$ has the normal structure and Zn^{2+} ions have a strong preference for A sites. Mixed ferrites may be prepared in which Zn^{2+} ions replace other divalent ions in an inverse ferrite. For example, cobalt ferrite is inverse, with Co^{2+} ions on B sites and Fe^{3+} ions equally divided between A and B sites. If some of the Co^{2+} is replaced by Zn^{2+} the zinc goes to A sites and Fe^{3+} is displaced to B sites. The B site moment is

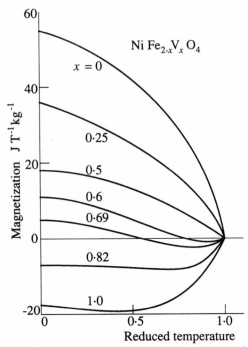

Figure 6.11 Measured spontaneous magnetization plotted against reduced temperature for a compensation-point ferrite system (after Blasse and Gorter, 1962, *J. Phys. Soc. Japan*, **17**, B1, 176).

Table 6.1 Characteristics of cations in spinel ferrites

Cation	Number of 3d electrons	Spin-only magnetic moment μ_B
Sc^{3+}	0	0
Ti^{3+}	1	1
$Ti^{2+}V^{3+}$	2	2
$V^{2+}Cr^{3+}$	3	3
$Cr^{2+}Mn^{3+}$	4	4
$Mn^{2+}Fe^{3+}$	5	5
$Fe^{2+}Co^{3+}$	6	4
$Co^{2+}Ni^{3+}$	7	3
Ni^{2+}	8	2
Cu^{2+}	9	1
$Cu^{+}Zn^{2+}$	10	0

therefore increased, unless its value is already at the maximum of $5+5 = 10\mu_B$, and the opposing A site moment is decreased by dilution by the non-magnetic Zn^{2+} ions. Thus we have the unusual situation that dilution by a nonmagnetic material increases the magnetic moment. The initial rate of rise of moment is such that extrapolation to fully substituted

Table 6.2 Calculated and experimental saturation magnetic moments in spinel ferrites

Material	Ion distribution		Sublattice moment		Saturation moment	
	A sites	B sites	A	B	Calc	Expt
$MnOFe_2O_3$	$Fe^{3+}_{0.2}Mn^{2+}_{0.8}$	$Mn^{2+}_{0.2}Fe^{3+}_{1.8}$	5	5+5	5	4·6
$FeOFe_2O_3$	Fe^{3+}	$Fe^{2+}Fe^{3+}$	5	4+5	4	4·1
$CoOFe_2O_3$	Fe^{3+}	$Co^{2+}Fe^{3+}$	5	3+5	3	3·7
$NiOFe_2O_3$	Fe^{3+}	$Ni^{2+}Fe^{3+}$	5	2+5	2	2·3
$CuOFe_2O_3$	Fe^{3+}	$Cu^{2+}Fe^{3+}$	5	1+5	1	1·3
$MgOFe_2O_3$	Fe^{3+}	$Mg^{+}Fe^{3+}$	5	0+5	0	1·1

$ZnO . Fe_2O_3$ (Fig. 6.12) leads to an expected moment of 10 μ_B per molecular unit. However, other factors come into play and pure (100%) zinc ferrite is non-magnetic.

In addition to the collinear ferrimagnetic structure described here, a so-called triangular structure can occur. The total energy is lower in these cases when some of the ionic magnetizations make an angle with each other that differs from 0° or 180°. Yafet and Kittel suggested that, where the A–A and B–B interactions are not small compared with A–B, the A and the B sublattices can be split further into A_1 and A_2, B_1 and B_2. Non-collinear angles occur between the magnetization vectors within A and B but the resultant magnetizations of A and B are still antiparallel.

6.2.6 Hexagonal ferrites

One range of ferrimagnetic oxides has the same hexagonal crystal structure as the mineral magnetoplumbite $PbFe_{12}O_{19}$. Various other elements may replace Pb. Most of these compounds are ferrimagnetic but some are antiferromagnetic. Barium ferrite $BaFe_{12}O_{19}$ is one of them which has been studied extensively. Its most important use is as a material for permanent magnets and it is known commercially as Ferroxdure. The ferrimagnetic members of this group of compounds have Curie temperatures between 500 K and 800 K. Their magnetic moments can be explained by the simple Néel model of ferrimagnetism in terms of the known occupation of the various lattice sites in the structure. The usefulness of barium ferrite for making permanent magnets lies in it having strong magnetic anisotropy with a preference for the magnetic moment to lie along the hexagonal c-axis. The coercivity is of the order of 0·3 T (300 Oe). In other ferrites of this general kind the anisotropy is different. The magnetization lies within the basal plane of the hexagonal structure. These are called by the commercial name Ferroxplane.

6.2.7 Ferrimagnetic garnets

This is another range of ferrimagnetic oxides having important applications. Their general formula is $R_3Fe_5O_{12}$, where R is a rare earth element

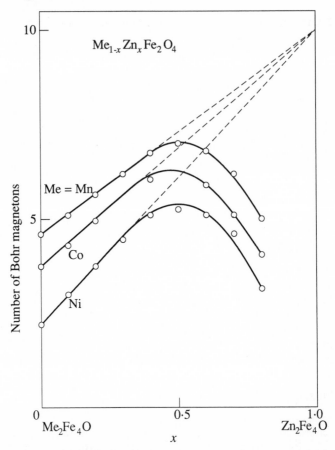

Figure 6.12 Measured saturation magnetic moment of manganese ferrite, cobalt ferrite and nickel ferrite diluted with zinc ferrite (after Guillaud, 1951, *J. Physique*, **12**, 239).

or yttrium. Yttrium is not strictly a rare earth but its chemical behaviour is like one and it is often loosely regarded as a rare earth.

The garnets have a complicated cubic crystal structure, with eight formula units per unit cell. The rare earth iron garnets are ferrimagnetic with Curie temperatures of about 550 K. The general formula can be represented by

$$\{C_3\}[A_2](D_3)O_{12}$$

where the cations are subdivided into three main sites with different crystallographic coordinations.

Yttrium iron garnet (YIG), $Y_3Fe_5O_{12}$ is an important technical material. It may be represented as

$$\{Y_3\}[Fe_2](Fe_3)O_{12}$$

The cation C has dodecahedral coordination and occupies the c crystallographic positions, of which there are 24: that is, {24c}.

The cation A has octahedral coordination and occupies the [16a] positions.

The cation D has tetrahedral coordination and occupies (24d) positions.

Which cations can occupy these sites is determined by their relative sizes. In general the rare earth ions go into {24c} sites.

The ferrimagnetic properties can be explained on a collinear model. The distribution of magnetic moments is written as R $\uparrow$ / $\downarrow$ Fe $\uparrow$ $_2$Fe $\downarrow$ $_3$O$_{12}$. The [a] and the (d)Fe^{3+} sublattices are antiparallel, their difference being one Fe^{3+} ion, or a moment of 5μ_B per formula unit. The R moment on {c} sites can be either parallel or antiparallel to the net iron moment, depending on the identity of R.

6.2.8 Applications of ferrimagnetic oxides

The technical applications of oxide ferrimagnets make use of their relatively large magnetization and their properties as insulators. An important use of magnetically soft spinel ferrites is for making cores for high frequency transformers and inductors in which there are no eddy current losses. Low-anisotropy garnets are used in devices operating at microwave frequencies. Hexagonal ferrites are widely used as permanent magnets, often in high frequency applications such as for electron beam control in TV and computer displays.

6.2.9 Mechanism of magnetic coupling in ferrimagnetic oxides

The source of the magnetic coupling in magnetic insulators is usually the process called superexchange. A non-magnetic anion such as oxygen takes part in a magnetic bond. A central anion interacts simultaneously with neighbouring magnetic cations and interposes a correlation between their directions of magnetization. The mechanism is described in more detail in Chapter 7.

6.3 Helimagnetism

So far we have dealt with simple collinear magnetic systems in which all the atomic magnetic moments in a domain lie parallel to or antiparallel to a single direction. These are common but special cases of a more general situation in which non-collinear arrangements occur.

The first material in which such behaviour was found was the intermetallic compound MnAu$_2$. This is one of a series of compounds formed at different stoichiometries across the gold–manganese alloy system. In weak applied fields the compound is apparently antiferromagnetic with a Néel temperature of 365 K. Under the influence of strong fields at temperatures below T_N it undergoes a transition to a quasi-ferromagnetic state. This kind of behaviour is known as metamagnetism and it is illustrated in Figures 6.13 and 6.14.

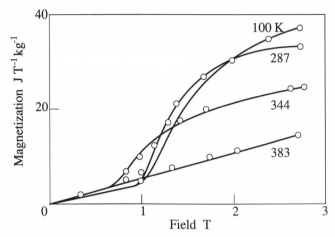

Figure 6.13 Experimental dependence of magnetization on field at different temperatures for MnAu$_2$, showing metamagnetic behaviour (after Meyer and Taglang, 1956, *J. Physique*, **17**, 457).

Neutron diffraction experiments have led to a clearer understanding of the magnetic properties. The pattern obtained from a powdered sample at a temperature well above T_N was consistent with coherent scattering by the Mn and Au nuclei alone, in their known (from X-ray diffraction) positions within the unit cell.

The crystal structure consists of a body-centred tetragonal arrangement of Mn atoms for which $c/a = 2·6$. Each Mn atom has two Au atoms near it, at a fixed distance above and below in the c-direction. Thus the manganese atoms are in layers perpendicular to the c axis, the interlayer distance being $c/2$.

At temperatures below T_N extra reflections of magnetic origin were present, occurring in pairs on either side of the respective nuclear reflections (Fig. 6.15). Their positions and intensities were found to be consistent with a spiral arrangement of magnetic moments on the Mn atoms. The screw axis is along the c-direction and the moments were found (at room temperature) to change their direction by 102 degrees for each repeat of the unit cell in the c-direction, or 51 degrees per layer of Mn atoms. The reasoning was as follows.

The normal condition for diffraction is

$$\sin \theta = \lambda/2 \, |G| \tag{6.22}$$

where $|G|$ is the magnitude of the reciprocal lattice vector

$$G = h\boldsymbol{\alpha} + k\boldsymbol{\beta} + l\boldsymbol{\gamma}$$

$\boldsymbol{\alpha}$, $\boldsymbol{\beta}$ and $\boldsymbol{\gamma}$ are the primitive translation vectors of the unit cell in reciprocal space. For a structure with a rectilinear unit cell,

$$|G| = (G_x^2 + G_y^2 + G_z^2)^{1/2} = (h^2/a^2 + k^2/b^2 + l^2/c^2)^{1/2} \tag{6.23}$$

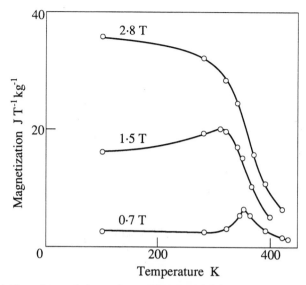

Figure 6.14 Experimental dependence of magnetization on temperature in three different field strengths, showing the effect of the collapse of the magnetic helix (after Meyer and Taglang, loc cit).

It was found that the magnetic part of the diffraction pattern could be explained if G was replaced by the vector sum $(G + v)$. The diagram in reciprocal space shown in Figure 6.16 illustrates what occurs. The scattering vector $|G + v|$ is the line drawn (in three dimensions) from the origin (000) to the respective points in the diagram. In the case of $MnAu_2$, v is a vector drawn in the c direction having a magnitude of 0.0324 Å^{-1} in reciprocal space. This corresponds in the real crystal (Fig. 6.16) to an arrangement of Mn magnetic moments all perpendicular to the c axis but rotating through a fixed angle for each Mn layer. The moment vector turns through a full circle to repeat itself in a distance of $0.0324^{-1} = 30.86 \text{ Å}$. The c dimension is 8.75 Å, so the turn angle per unit cell is $360 \times 8.75/30.86 = 102$ degrees, or 51 degrees per Mn layer.

Applying strong magnetic fields causes a rearrangement of magnetic moments. The moments remain within planes perpendicular to the c axis but they turn under the influence of the field so that the quasi-ferromagnetic state is reached eventually. Whether they turn continuously or whether an increasing proportion flips suddenly to the collinear arrangement is an open question.

6.3.1 Other non-collinear structures

Many other materials are now known to possess strange magnetic structures. Pure chromium is one of these. Its magnetic susceptibility varies little with temperature, actually increasing with increasing temperature,

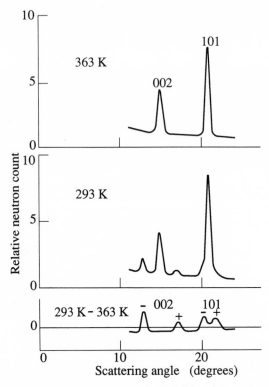

Figure 6.15 Neutron diffraction patterns of MnAu₂ (after Herpin and Meriel, 1961, *J. Physique*, **22**, 337).

but there is a small kink at 310 K (Fig. 6.8). The specific heat has a λ-type anomaly at the same temperature, suggestive of a magnetic order–disorder transition. The structure is basically antiferromagnetic, with the magnetic moments at the cube corners and the cube centres of the body centred cubic structure mutually opposed. Domains of magnetization exist such that in traversing a line of atoms normal to the (100) plane, the direction of the atomic magnetic moments changes sign every *n* atoms. The width of the domains varies with temperature, ranging from 22 to 26 unit cells. Also, above 150 K the direction of the magnetization is parallel to the antiphase domain boundaries, along cube edges in the $\langle 100 \rangle$ direction. On cooling through 150 K it flips discontinuously to lie perpendicular to the domain walls. The magnetic moment per chromium atom in this structure is about $0 \cdot 45 \mu_B$.

Chromium forms ferromagnetic (f) and antiferromagnetic (a) compounds with other elements. Examples are CrSb(a), CrAs(f), Cr₂As(f), CrS(f), CrSe(a), CrTe(f), CrGe(f) and CrBr₃(f).

Elemental manganese is weakly antiferromagnetic with a Néel temperature of 100 K. Many alloys and compounds containing manganese are strongly ferromagnetic or antiferromagnetic. The first metallic antiferro-

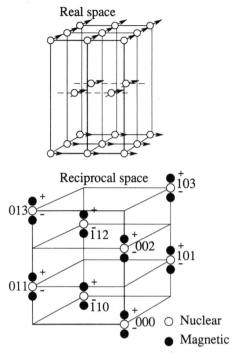

Figure 6.16 Magnetic structure of MnAu$_2$ at low temperature, in real space and in reciprocal space.

magnet to be discovered (1957) was a copper–manganese alloy. Pure vanadium possesses some physical properties which have led to speculation that it might be weakly antiferromagnetic, but this has not been confirmed.

6.3.2 Unusual magnetic materials

The intermetallic compound ZrZn$_2$ is ferromagnetic. Its Curie temperature is 21 K and its magnetic moment is $0.13\mu_B$ per ZrZn$_2$ unit (Fig. 3.7). There is still no reliable evidence as to where the magnetism resides in the structure, although it is suspected that ZrZn$_2$ is an itinerant ferromagnet with the moment diffused throughout the structure. Neither Zr nor Zn is known to possess a localized magnetic moment in any other context.

An equally surprising material is the alloy of scandium and indium which contains 24 per cent of indium. This alloy is apparently a disordered solid solution and it becomes ferromagnetic below 6 K. Its moment is small, about $0.05\mu_B$ per scandium atom. No explanation has yet been given as to how ferromagnetism can arise in this alloy. It exists over a very narrow range of composition, suggesting that the kind of ferromagnetism that it represents might be a more general phenomenon than appears at first sight, because the probability of finding it is so low.

6.4 The rare earth metals

6.4.1 Crystal structures

The rare earths are the elements with atomic numbers from 57 to 71. In the free atom the extra-nuclear electrons occupy energy levels up to 6s, with the exception of the 4f shell, which provides vacancies for a total of 14 electrons, and the 5d shell. The 4f shell contains a variable number of electrons through the series and the 5d shell is either empty or nearly so. Element 61, promethium, has no stable isotopes and it does not occur naturally.

In most of the periodic families of the elements, increase in the atomic number is associated with an increase in the atomic or ionic size. The addition of extra electrons to successively higher energy levels has more influence than the naturally contracting effect of increasing the nuclear charge. As shown in Figure 6.17, following the rare earth series from lanthanum (Z = 57) to lutetium (Z = 71) is associated with an anomalous decrease in size. This is known as the lanthanide contraction. The electrons in the incomplete 4f shell act as magnetic electrons and in the atoms of all the rare earth elements they are screened from outside influences by a considerable density of charge. The lanthanide contraction occurs because the expected effect on the atomic size of changing the 4f occupation is suppressed by this screening and the diminishing effect of the nuclear charge dominates.

The various kinds of crystal structure that occur in the rare earths tend to

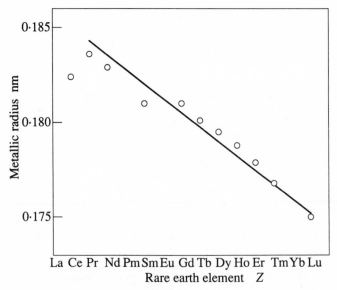

Figure 6.17 Atomic radius for rare earth metals as a function of atomic number, illustrating the lanthanide contraction.

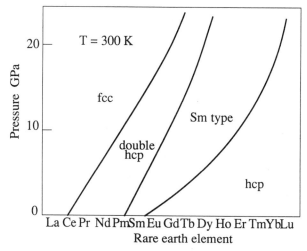

Figure 6.18 Unified phase diagram for rare earths, showing the effect of pressure.

be close-packed structures or minor deviations from close-packing, or with different stacking sequences. Moving from one to another structure with changing atomic number is dominated by changes in the overlap of atomic wave functions as the atomic size changes. The same effect can be produced by applying hydrostatic pressure. At increased pressure the overlap increases and the behaviour of a lighter element is simulated, the effect being the same as with a reduction in nuclear charge. There is an overall uniformity in the structural behaviour, as the graph showing structure as a function of pressure and atomic number in Figure 6.18 illustrates. It is the properties of the outer electrons, higher than 4f, that control the crystallography.

6.4.2 Magnetism in rare earths

In the solid state the orbital magnetic moment is not usually suppressed significantly by the effects of the crystalline electric fields. In the metals there appears to be no question of appreciable charge overlap between 4f electrons of adjacent atoms, and the magnetic electrons are probably in sharp atomic-like energy levels and not in energy bands of significant width. So far as the high temperature paramagnetic properties of the rare earth metals are concerned there is usually no great difference in magnetic behaviour between the metal and its salts, in cases where the atoms are ionized to a like degree. Nearly all the rare earths exhibit magnetic order of some kind. The heavier ones, from gadolinium (number 64, with seven 4f electrons) to lutetium (number 71, with 14 4f electrons) exhibit complicated forms of magnetism but the lighter ones, from lanthanum (number 57, zero 4f electrons) to europium (number 63, six 4f electrons) are much more complicated.

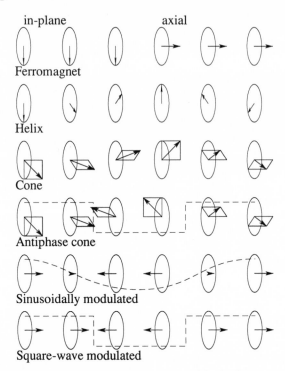

Figure 6.19 Variety of magnetic structures found in the heavy rare earths.

6.4.3 Magnetic structures of the heavier rare earth metals

All the heavier rare earth elements except ytterbium (Yb) exhibit states of magnetic order when in the form of the pure metal. Some have the same helical structure as that found in $MnAu_2$.

The structures have been determined by neutron diffraction experiments on single crystals of the metal, by extensions of the method described in Chapter 4. The kinds of magnetic structure found are shown in Figure 6.19.

Only Gd is simply ferromagnetic in the magnetically ordered state. Tb and Dy are ferromagnetic at low temperatures but change to a simple helix at higher temperatures before becoming paramagnetic finally. Ho has a cone structure at low temperature and a helix at higher temperature. Er has a cone structure at the lowest temperature. On heating it has sequentially an antiphase modulated cone structure, a sinusoidally modulated collinear structure and finally it becomes paramagnetic. Tm has a square-wave modulated collinear structure at the lowest temperature, becoming sinusoidally modulated collinear and then paramagnetic. The structures and transition temperatures are summarized in Figure 6.20.

The kind of exchange interaction giving rise to helical and other periodically modulated structures is discussed in Chapter 7.

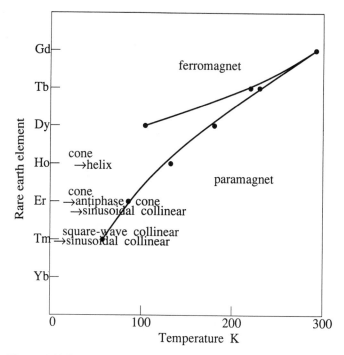

Figure 6.20 Low temperature magnetic structures in rare earths.

6.4.4 Magnetic structures of the lighter rare earth metals

These elements are even more complicated. As an example, when neodymium is cooled below its Néel temperature of 19·9 K its magnetic structure undergoes a series of transitions, with different ordering wave vectors. At first the ordering occurs predominantly on the hexagonal sites of the double hexagonal close packed structure and then, below 8·3 K, ordering starts on the cubic sites. In zero magnetic field this sequence eventually forms at the lowest temperatures a phase which has four inequivalent modulating wave vectors. This structure distorts when a strong magnetic field is applied into an even more complicated magnetically ordered phase which gives a neutron diffraction pattern containing a sequence of many satellites to the main reflections. The full solution to the magnetic structure has not yet been achieved. The other light rare earth elements are similarly complicated.

6.5 Spin glasses

A spin glass is a solid material, usually a dilute magnetic alloy, in which there are spin magnetic moments which compete with each other. The components are frozen below a certain critical freezing temperature into a random distribution. In general these materials are crystalline. They are not the same as metallic glasses or glassy metals, which are amorphous and are discussed in Section 6.6.

Spin glasses exhibit unusual properties. They have a sharp cusp in the AC susceptibility measured in a weak field, occurring at the freezing temperature T_f. There is no contribution to the magnetic diffraction pattern observed with neutrons which would indicate any long range magnetic order. The specific heat exhibits no magnetic anomaly at T_f but there is a broad maximum well above T_f. At temperatures below T_f the magnetization and the susceptibility depend strongly on the exact experimental conditions employed. Cooling through T_f in a strong magnetic field has a very marked effect on the magnetization.

The well-known spin glass systems are dilute magnetic alloys in which there are stable magnetic moments in a non-magnetic or nearly magnetic host metal. Examples are **CuMn**, **AuFe**, **AuMn**, **PtFe**.

The concentration range in which spin glass properties are observed is fairly limited. Above a certain concentration full long range magnetic order sets in. **AuFe** becomes ferromagnetic and **CuMn** becomes antiferromagnetic. In some systems it is possible to find an alloy composition which with decreasing temperature exhibits first paramagnetism, then full ferromagnetic order, and at the lowest temperature a spin glass state.

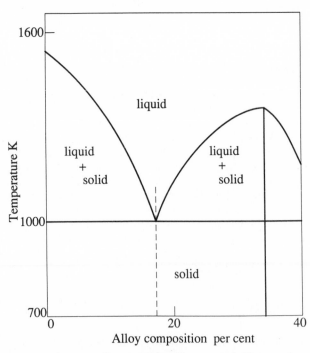

Figure 6.21 Schematic phase diagrams for a glassy metal alloy system, showing the deep eutectic.

At the lowest concentrations the spin glass state is limited by the limits of a percolation mechanism.

A full theoretical account of all the experimental properties of spin glasses has yet to be given. The models which have been developed depend on a long range dependence of magnetic interactions becoming weak at long distances from a magnetic atom. The interactions between the small regions of stronger order are too weak to overcome the disordering influences.

6.6 Magnetic amorphous alloys

It is possible to produce amorphous metals by rapidly cooling certain alloys from the molten state. To all appearances these materials have the same frozen-in liquid structure as ordinary glass. Some of these amorphous alloys are ferromagnetic. They are excellent soft magnetic materials having a wide range of technological applications. They also represent a challenge to the scientific understanding of magnetic materials, since most of the existing theories of solids assume lattice periodicity.

6.6.1 Production of metallic glasses

The crystallization of a liquid is a kinetic process involving the nucleation of crystalline embryos and their growth. If the rate of cooling from the liquid state is fast enough a liquid can be frozen to a glassy state before the bulk of it becomes crystallized. The calculated critical cooling rate for some pure metallic elements is about $10^{10}\,\mathrm{K\,s^{-1}}$. This is much higher than is available from current methods of cooling (about $10^6\,\mathrm{K\,s^{-1}}$), so amorphous pure metallic elements cannot be produced by liquid quenching. This is also true for most alloys. However, many alloys exist which for limited ranges of composition form stable glasses when they are cooled through the melting temperature at a rate of 10^5 to $10^6\,\mathrm{K\,s^{-1}}$. The most favourable alloys are those near a eutectic point in the binary phase diagram (Fig. 6.21).

The most common method used for rapid cooling uses melt-spinning. A jet of molten liquid is squirted out of a small nozzle on to a rapidly rotating smooth metal disc. A long ribbon of amorphous metal is produced which has uniform geometry. Typically the thickness of the ribbon is a few tens of micrometres and for laboratory conditions the width is about 2 mm. Ribbons up to about 100 mm wide are produced commercially using sophisticated nozzle arrangements. The ribbons are notable for their high mechanical strength.

Systems of alloys of the greatest magnetic interest are combinations of a transition metal (usually iron), and one or more of the metalloids B, P or Si.

6.6.2 Magnetism in amorphous alloys

Most magnetic states found in crystalline materials have also been found in amorphous alloys, though with detailed differences. Because there is no magnetocrystalline anisotropy, one of the factors that prevents some materials from being soft ferromagnets is removed.

However glasses are not free from anisotropy of some kind because in the rapidly quenched state they contain locked-in stresses which have influence through the magnetostriction. When the composition is such that there is little magnetostriction the coercivity is usually very low and the permeability high. Such materials are ideally suited for use in such devices as transformer cores. They have the additional advantage of having high electrical resistance, so avoiding eddy current losses.

6.7 High-T_C superconducting ceramics

Conventional superconductivity relates to some metals that are known to become superconducting at temperatures below about 20 K. Such materials are well understood in terms of the theory of Bardeen, Cooper and Schrieffer (BCS), the essential ingredient of which is a quasi-particle called a Cooper pair. This is formed as a result of a special kind of electron–phonon interaction.

Since 1986 a new range of materials has been found which superconduct up to temperatures of about 100 K and which are essentially ceramics. There are relatively minor differences between their compositions, but a typical one is the compound $YBa_2Cu_3O_7$. As yet the reason for the superconductivity is not understood. Orthodox BCS theory appears to be incapable of explaining the relatively high values of T_C. The nature of the quasi-particles acting here is not known. The existence of layers in the crystal structure containing Cu and O atoms seems to be important. These layers appear to contain regions of magnetic spin density. When the distribution of this spin density is examined using neutrons with an external magnetic field applied, it varies markedly with temperature and is very different above and below T_C. It seems likely that the nature of the electronic interactions which give rise to the quasi-particles will be found to be of magnetic origin. The results of further research in this area are awaited with great interest.

What is in no doubt at all is that these high-T_C superconductors are of great technological importance and that many device applications will follow in the near future.

Chapter 7 ⎯⎯⎯⎯⎯⎯⎯⎯

Exchange interactions in magnetism and hyperfine fields

7.1 Exchange interactions in magnetism

So far we have discussed the effects of ferromagnetic and antiferromagnetic order in solids in terms of molecular fields, without attempting to explain the origins of the molecular fields. Dipole–dipole magnetic interactions between local magnetic moments are far too weak to explain the effects observed. Curie temperatures in strong ferromagnets can be more than 1000 K, so that a thermal energy of $kT_C \simeq 10^{-7}$ J per atom is necessary to destroy the magnetically ordered state. The dipole ineraction energy is of the order of μ_B^2/a^3, about 10^{-9} J per atom since the interatomic separation a is about 0·1 nm (1 Å). The dipole interactions can therefore be at the most only a correction to the primary effect.

7.1.1 Heisenberg direct exchange between moments localized on atoms

The idea of exchange coupling between the spins of two or more atoms first appeared clearly in the work of Heitler and London (1927) on chemical binding. It was applied by Heisenberg (1928) to the theory of ferromagnetism. This gave the first explanation of an interaction energy of the correct order of magnitude. It is essentially an electrostatic effect. The relative directions of two interacting spins for quantum mechanical reasons cannot be changed without changing the spatial distribution of charge. The resulting changes in the Coulomb electrostatic energy of the whole system act as though there is a direct coupling between the directions of the spins involved.

We may consider the lobes of charge density corresponding to different electron states in a single free atom and what happens when two such atoms are near to each other. There is a tendency to form overlap regions of charge density contributed by both atoms and the Pauli exclusion principle must be applied to the region of overlap. No single electron state may be occupied twice. When the orbital wave function is symmetrical the spin one must be antisymmetrical and vice versa. Changing the spin symmetry by the reversal of one spin must change the orbital symmetry and this redistributes charge. A correlation between the electron spins of the two atoms is imposed. The effect is as though there were an interaction energy between the spin vectors proportional to their scalar product $S_1 . S_2$. When the Schrödinger equation of the system is written there is a Heisenberg contribution to the total Hamiltonian

$$\mathcal{H}_{\text{Heis}} = -2J_{12}S_1 . S_2 \tag{7.1}$$

This case of two neighbouring atoms is that of the hydrogen molecule and its properties are well known. An embryonic molecular ferromagnetism would occur if the exchange constant J_{12} was positive. This is a triplet state, with magnetic quantum numbers M of $-1,0$ and $+1$. A molecular antiferromagnet occurs for negative J_{12}. This is a singlet state having only the magnetic quantum number $M = 0$. For the hydrogen molecule J_{12} is always negative, for all values of the distance of separation between the constituent atoms (Fig. 7.1). Here the triplet state would have an energy greater than that of the two separate atoms and is therefore not favoured.

In an actual three-dimensional solid in which a given atom is surrounded by many others it is necessary to sum the effect of the exchange over all the interactions which can contribute. The Heisenberg Hamiltonian becomes

$$\mathcal{H}_{\text{Heis}} = -2\sum_{i,j}J_{ij}S_i . S_j \tag{7.2}$$

Mostly we are concerned only with interaction between neighbours, and the part of the Hamiltonian that concerns us is

$$\mathcal{H}' = -2J \sum_{\text{neighbours}} S_i . S_j \tag{7.3}$$

J is the exchange integral between adjacent atoms and the summation

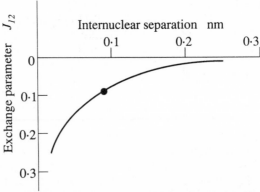

Figure 7.1 Exchange interaction parameter of the hydrogen molecule as a function of the separation between the two hydrogen nuclei. The black dot marks the equilibrium separation.

extends over all neighbouring pairs of atoms. Closed shells of electrons contribute nothing to this equation. Exchange effects between electrons of the same atom merely give an additive constant to the energy of the whole system.

In principle the exchange integral can have either sign. A positive value for J leads to ferromagnetism and a negative value leads to antiferromagnetism or ferrimagnetism. However, this statement has really only the status of being a plausible postulate. No rigorous theoretical treatment has yet shown why J should have both the correct sign and the correct magnitude to explain the known ferromagnetic properties of common ferromagnets such as iron, nickel and cobalt. The question remains of why J should be positive in iron when it is definitely negative in the much simpler case of the hydrogen molecule. Watson, Freeman and Nesbet (1962), found J to be about two orders of magnitude too small to account for the measured Curie temperature of nickel and to have the wrong sign. It is very unlikely that direct exchange between localized electrons can be the main origin of the ferromagnetism in metals of the iron group.

There are even greater difficulties in considering the rare earth metals. The 4f electron shells, the radii of which are about 0·03 nm (0·3 Å), cannot overlap significantly between neighbouring atoms, which are about 0·3 nm (3 Å) apart. Also, the 4f electrons are well screened (see Fig. 2.7).

It would appear, therefore, that while the basic mechanism of direct exchange between moments localized on atoms is a possibility for magnetic interactions in solids, it is unlikely to operate in its simplest form except in a very few materials.

7.1.2 Exchange effects between collective electrons

So far in this chapter we have been considering exchange between localized magnetic moments. This model can have little relevance to magnetic interactions between electrons described by bands and moving relatively freely throughout a metal.

There is still considerable doubt about how the exchange energy arises in metals in which the ferromagnetism is due to electrons in a partly filled band of strongly 3d-like character. Different authors have expressed apparently equally valid diverging opinions.

One point of view is as follows. Various factors operate which tend to keep electrons apart. One of them is ordinary Coulomb repulsion between like charges. These are called correlation effects. The correlation energy for 3d-band electrons is difficult to estimate and it is of uncertain magnitude. This view assumes that the correlation energy is not large enough to prevent magnetic carriers (either electrons or electron holes) from coming together on the same atom. The origin of the ferromagnetism would then be the kind of intra-atomic exchange coupling that is responsible for Hund's rules and dominates the arrangement of electrons in atoms. This provides a means whereby throughout the metal a state with unpaired electrons having parallel spins has a lower energy than otherwise.

We introduce a quantity ΔE, which is the energy required to reverse the direction of the spin of an electron without changing its wave number, at the absolute zero of temperature. This is the same as the displacement in energy of the sub-band with positive spin relative to that with negative spin, when the magnetization is saturated. The state with spins parallel will always have the lower energy in order to satisfy Hund's rules, tending towards ferromagnetism. But this needs to overcome the small increase in the Fermi energy resulting from setting up a magnetic moment. The condition for ferromagnetism is

$$(2/n)\Delta E\nu(E_m)V > 1 \tag{7.4}$$

where $\nu(E_m)$ is the density of states at the Fermi level, V is the atomic volume and n is the excess number of spins per atom pointing in the direction of magnetization. This is really the condition that the total energy is lowered by a small polarization at the Fermi surface. An estimate of the value for the left hand side of Equation (7.4) based on experimental quantities gives 1·23 for nickel and 1·11 for iron, both of which thus satisfy this condition for ferromagnetism. The condition suggests that ferromagnetism should occur most readily when the density of states at the Fermi level is large, and when ΔE is relatively large. Under the conditions assumed here it would be expected that ΔE would be given by the product of

(a) the energy difference, known experimentally from spectroscopic measurements, between the states of the free atom for which two spins of electrons in an incomplete d shell are parallel or antiparallel, and

(b) the probability that an electron with a given direction of spin finds itself on the same atom as another electron with a spin that may be parallel or antiparallel.

Rough calculations of values for ΔE made along these lines for iron and for nickel show quite reasonable agreement with the experimental estimates.

Once the existence of ΔE has been justified, the general basis of collective electron ferromagnetism becomes more sound. Comparing the nomenclature here with that of Chapter 3, ΔE is the same as $2k\theta'$. However, it is true to say that the question of exchange in electron bands which are relatively narrow, like those of 3d metals, has not yet been solved satisfactorily. Other views concern what happens if the correlation energy is large and two magnetic carriers are inhibited from coming together on the same atom. Intra-atomic effects are then insignificant. It has not yet been possible to distinguish experimentally between the validity of the different points of view.

The experimental observations that is almost universally true is that magnetic moments occur in the first transition series for elements at the top end of the series; Cr, Mn, Fe, Co and Ni. Two puzzling exceptions are the intermetallic compound $ZrZn_2$ and a particular scandium–indium alloy. Of these Ni and Co are strong ferromagnets, Fe is a weak ferromagnet, Mn is a collinear antiferromagnet and Cr is a (marginal) sinusoidal antiferromagnet.

7.1.3 Superexchange

The magnetic coupling in many magnetic oxides and other similar materials cannot be explained by the mechanism of direct exchange because the ions on which the magnetic moment is known to be located are too far apart. Also, when the crystal structures of such materials are examined it is often found that a non-magnetic anion such as oxygen is situated in the line joining magnetic cations. If the materials are insulators, band mechanisms requiring fairly free transfer of electrons throughout the solid are not likely to operate. Kramers (1934) and Anderson (1950) proposed a mechanism called superexchange. Spins of magnetic cations are coupled indirectly through intervening anions.

Superexchange is thought to operate in the antiferromagnetic compound MnO (Fig. 7.2). Its crystal structure is that of sodium chloride. Mn^{2+} ions form a face-centred cubic structure which is interpenetrated by an identical face-centred cubic structure of O^{2-} ions. Mn^{2+} ions which are next nearest neighbours have spins which are always antiparallel to each other. Lines joining these second neighbours always contain an anion O^{2-} at the mid-point. First neighbour Mn^{2+} ions are not strongly correlated and no anion lies directly between them. The important interaction is through the anion, which in this case has its outer electrons in a p-state. The p-wave functions (charge density) extend outwards from the anion in opposing lobes (Fig. 7.3a). Each lobe represents a total of one electron per anion. The two electrons thus represented, one on each side, must have opposite spins in order to satisfy the Pauli exclusion principle. These lobes overlap with, and mix with, lobes of d-electrons extending out from each Mn^{2+} cation. Only mixing of the same spin is possible. This covalent mixing is of

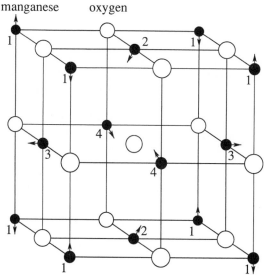

Figure 7.2 The magnetic structure of antiferromagnetic MnO. Members of the four manganese sublattices are numbered. Nearest members of the same sublattice are strongly correlated through intervening oxygen atoms.

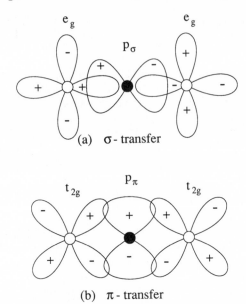

(a) σ - transfer

(b) π - transfer

Figure 7.3 Schematic electron change distribution round interacting cations and anions in superexchange coupling by σ-transfer and π-transfer.

the same kind as that which forms the binding mechanism of many semiconducting solids. This mechanism thus lowers the total energy when the Mn^{2+} cations on each side have their spins oppositely oriented, and provides a driving force towards antiferromagnetism which is strong in the line containing the anion.

While the mechanism described is correct in principle, the detailed situation is more complicated. The lobes representing the two 2p electrons of O^{2-} may stretch along the bond (p_σ) or perpendicular to it (p_Π). And the question of the symmetry of the 3d electron distribution of the cations arises. The d-electrons may be divided into a three-fold degenerate state called t_{2g} and a two-fold degenerate state called e_g. This is the Mulliken notation. There is an equivalent but rather different Bethe notation. The lobes of the t_{2g} state extend along the diagonals of an imaginary cube surrounding the ion. The lobes of the e_g state are mutually perpendicular. Whether the e_g or the t_{2g} state has the lower energy and is preferentially occupied depends on several factors, including the crystallographic environment of the cation.

There are therefore different kinds of superexchange interaction, illustrated in Figures 7.3a and 7.3b. Electron transfer can only take place between a p_σ orbital and the e_g orbital of principal overlap (called σ-transfer), or between a p_Π orbital and the t_{2g} orbital of principal overlap (called Π-transfer).

For a given interatomic separation the orbital overlap involved in σ-transfer is greater than it is in Π-transfer, as Figure 7.3 would seem to indicate. A σ-transfer process is therefore the stronger. In a given situation, depending on the circumstances either or both σ- or Π-transfer may operate, with corresponding variations in the strength of the overall superexchange interaction. By and large, theory based along the lines indicated offers a good explanation of magnetic interactions in non-metallic magnetically ordered materials.

Processes may sometimes be modified by the operation of cation–anion–cation interactions at 90° or other angles different from 180°. In special cases there may be direct overlap of the diagonal t_{2g} orbitals of first neighbour cations, or between t_{2g} of one atom and e_g of the other. This is direct exchange. It would generally be a relatively weak contribution to the total effect which depends on separation and it might be positive (ferro-magnetic) or negative (antiferromagnetic) in sign.

7.1.4 Indirect exchange by polarization of the conduction electrons

An important mechanism of magnetic coupling between localized magnetic moments in metals depends on the ability of conduction electrons to interact magnetically with the local moments and to propagate between different magnetic sites. How the conduction electrons can polarize and propagate was first shown by Ruderman and Kittel (1954). They dealt with nuclear magnetic moments immersed in a distribution of conduction electrons. Kasuya and then Yosida developed and extended the theory to s–f and s–d interactions. The mechanism has become known as the RKKY theory. The spin polarization of the conduction electrons is not localized in the vicinity of the local moment but is oscillatory and is of long range. The mechanism can be visualized simply as follows.

Consider a single localized magnetic moment surrounded by a gas of conduction electrons. The local moment is on a lattice site in the metal. The effect of the local moment is to make the site on which it is placed a region favourable for a conduction electron of parallel magnetic moment but unfavourable for an electron of antiparallel moment. In order to take advantage of the magnetic interaction, a parallel electron will distort its wave function so as to be larger in the vicinity of the local moment. This is brought about by mixing in other electron states of the same spin orientation. The result is as though only states above the Fermi level are added. The wave functions of the added states are such that they are all in phase with each other at the position of the local moment, so that they interfere constructively at that point. Since they must correspond to a range of wave vectors and therefore a range of wavelengths, they must get out of step as the distance from the local moment increases, and begin to interfere destructively (Fig. 7.4a). The original uniform distribution of electrons with parallel spin is changed to have an oscillatory behaviour which dies out as the distance from the local moment increases.

Likewise, conduction electrons with antiparallel spin distort their wave functions so as to be smaller in the vicinity of the local moment. In just the same way this produces a corresponding oscillatory absence of antiparallel

(a)

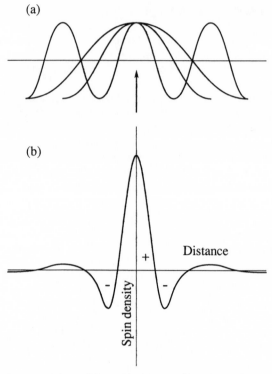

(b)

Distance

Spin density

Figure 7.4 RKKY interactions; (a) shows the wavefunctions of interacting conduction electrons near a magnetic impurity, (b) shows the resultant distribution of conduction electron spin density.

spin. The overall effect is to give an oscillatory distribution of spin density in the region of the local moment (Fig. 7.4b). Since the attraction of electrons with parallel spin is exactly matched by the repulsion of those with antiparallel spin at all points, and all have the same charge, the distribution of charge density remains uniform throughout. The periodicity of the spin density oscillation is set by the wavelengths of the conduction electrons at the Fermi level. That is, it is dominated by the Fermi momentum. The exact form of the spin density distribution and its variation with distance must depend on how the electron wavelength varies with energy at the Fermi level, which is given by the (E,k) relationship. The RKKY theory was worked out for free electrons having a spherical Fermi surface and as such represents a simplification. More complicated situations have not yet been investigated widely.

When a second atom bearing a local magnetic moment is situated at an arbitrary distance from the first it interacts ferromagnetically or antiferromagnetically depending on whether it is in a positive or a negative part of the polarization wave from the first atom. According to the RKKY theory the strength of the magnetic coupling between atoms at a relatively large distance R apart varies according to

$$(1/R^3) \cos(2k_F R) \tag{7.5}$$

where k_F is the Fermi momentum.

The most important properties of this mechanism of magnetic coupling are the following. First, the magnetic interaction has a long range character, certainly of much longer range than any direct exchange involving charge overlap between adjacent atoms. Second, quite large variations in the strength of the interaction and even reversal of its sign are possible with small changes in the relationship between the interatomic distance and the periodicity of the spin density. The overall effect is important in determining the properties of some spin glasses.

7.1.5 Experimental confirmation of the RKKY model

The RKKY model appears to apply well to some dilute magnetic alloys, such as dilute solutions of manganese in copper. The manganese atoms are probably in either $3d^4$ or $3d^5$ states, carrying corresponding local magnetic moments of $4\mu_B$ or $5\mu_B$. At a concentration of about $0\cdot01$ atomic per cent of Mn each manganese atom is surrounded on average by $(0\cdot01$ per cent$)^{-1} = 10^4$ copper atoms, or in a face-centred cubic structure (4 atoms per unit cell) by 2500 unit cells. These would be contained in a sphere of radius about thirteen times the lattice parameter. Such an alloy is antiferromagnetic at low temperatures. This was the alloy system to which Yosida first applied the theory and it satisfactorily explained the detailed experimental observations on the nuclear magnetic resonance and the electron spin resonance properties. Also, Kondo showed that the interaction of the kind described gave a natural description of the minima in graphs of electrical resistance against temperature for many dilute alloys.

In the rare earth metals there is little possibility of direct overlap interactions between the 4f electrons of adjacent atoms. These electrons are too well screened and the radius of their shells is relatively small. Indirect exchange through the conduction electrons allows them to become magnetically ordered. The spiral and other non-collinear magnetic structures that are fairly common in the rare earths and their alloys are a result of varying strengths and signs of interaction at different interatomic neighbour distances.

7.1.6 Magnetic interactions which differ between different atomic neighbours

It is clearly to be expected that when the magnetic interaction is of long range and its strength depends on the interatomic distance, there will be situations in which the nearest neighbour interaction does not dominate the others completely. Sometimes significant interactions might be expected to have opposite signs. Under certain conditions helical magnetic structures can result.

A crystal structure having uniaxial symmetry, such as a hexagonal or a tetragonal structure, is the simplest case to consider. The magnetic atoms are arranged in parallel layers perpendicular to the c-axis. A simplifying assumption is that magnetocrystalline anisotropy acts to confine the atomic moments to lie within the planes of the layers. The exchange coupling constants J_n are defined as follows:

> J_0 refers to pairs of atoms in the same layer (assumed positive here),
> J_1 refers to pairs of atoms each situated in adjacent layers,
> J_2 refers to pairs of atoms each situated in second nearest layers,
> and so on.

These exchange constants can be regarded in a molecular field model a being equivalent to molecular field coefficients $\gamma_0, \gamma_1, \gamma_2, \ldots$ The angle between the spin directions of adjacent layers is α, and it is not now assumed that this is necessarily $0°$ or $180°$. The total molecular field acting on the atoms of the central layer is now

$$(B_0)_{mol} = \gamma_0 \sigma_0 + 2\gamma_1 \sigma_1 \cos \alpha + 2\gamma_2 \sigma_2 \cos 2\alpha + \ldots \tag{7.6}$$

where σ_n is the magnetization of the nth layer. There are equivalent neighbouring layers both above and below the central layer. If all the layers are equivalent, their magnetizations are the same and $\sigma_0 = \sigma_1 = \ldots$ Then

$$(B_0)_{mol} = \sigma(\gamma_0 + 2\gamma_1 \cos \alpha + 2\gamma_2 \cos 2\alpha + \ldots) = \sigma\gamma(\alpha) \tag{7.7}$$

Since the exchange energy is the self energy of the magnetic moment in the molecular field

$$E_{ex} = -\int_0^\sigma B_0 \, d\sigma = -1/2\gamma(\alpha)\sigma^2 \tag{7.8}$$

This varies with temperature through the dependence of the magnetization on temperature. At a given temperature, the equilibrium interlayer turn angle α_0 is that value for which the exchange energy is a minimum. This is where $\gamma(\alpha) = (\gamma_0 + 2\gamma_1 \cos \alpha + 2\gamma_2 \cos 2\alpha + \ldots)$ is a maximum.

If $\gamma_1, \gamma_2, \ldots$ are all positive the maximum value of $\gamma(\alpha)$ is where $\alpha_0 = 0$. This is a ferromagnetic state, with all the layers magnetized in the same direction. If γ_1 is negative and $\gamma_2, \gamma_3, \ldots$ are all zero, the maximum value of $\gamma(\alpha)$ is where $\cos \alpha = -1$, or $\alpha = 180°$. This is simple antiferromagnetism, with the spins of alternate layers pointing in opposite directions. When $\gamma_3, \gamma_4, \ldots$ are insignificant, with γ_1 and γ_2 of opposite sign and γ_2 having a magnitude at least $\gamma_1/4$ the magnetic structure is helical.

The interlayer turn angle α_0 is given by

$$\cos \alpha_0 = -\gamma_1/4\gamma_2 \tag{7.9}$$

Different external constraints and initial conditions give rise to different magnetic structures, and the complication of the treatment increases as higher orders of neighbour interaction become significant. Not all the structures are non-collinear. Some of the more complicated antiferromagnetic structures are fairly well understood in terms of particular relationships between higher neighbour interactions.

In metals the principal mechanism by which significant interactions of either sign between a central atom and it neighbours at different distances can occur is the RKKY mechanism.

7.2 Hyperfine interactions in magnetic materials

Hyperfine interactions are interactions between atomic nuclei and the electrons that surround them. Their name arises from the way in which the interactions were first observed, by their effect on spectra in the visible region of the spectrum. The interactions may be studied by making observations on nuclear properties, using a variety of experimental techniques. They give sometimes overlapping and sometimes complementary information about the properties of extranuclear electrons and about the solid state interactions which involve these electrons.

The three main properties are the following.

(1) The magnetic interaction between the nucleus and the electrons, which depends linearly on the nuclear spin I and is expressed as the hyperfine magnetic field B_H. This can be thought of as the effective magnetic field acting at the location of the nucleus. Thus we have a sensitive probe placed right inside the atomic structure which reacts to effects on the atomic scale as distinct from taking large-scale averages. It should be noted that this hyperfine field is quite different from the Weiss molecular field, or any other molecular field which expresses the exchange interaction in magnetically ordered systems.

(2) The electrostatic interaction between the nucleus and the electrons, which varies in a quadratic way with the nuclear spin. It is the nuclear quadrupole interaction, between the nuclear quadrupole moment (if it is not zero) and the gradient of the electric field in which it is situated.

(3) The electron density (not the spin density) at the probe nucleus, which is observed as the isomer shift in experiments using the Mössbauer effect.

Information on hyperfine interactions comes from experiments on effects such as the Mössbauer effect, nuclear magnetic resonance and nuclear specific heats.

7.2.1 The Mössbauer effect

The Mössbauer effect arises from a special property of the emission and absorption of gamma rays by nuclei of atoms that are bound in a crystal lattice. It leads essentially to a form of spectroscopy having a much higher intrinsic resolving power than that of any other form of spectroscopy.

When a free atom at rest emits a gamma ray photon it recoils with kinetic energy

$$R = E_0^2/2Mc^2$$

where E_0 is the energy of the nuclear transition, M is the mass of the atom and c is the velocity of light. The emitted gamma ray photon thus has the energy $E_\gamma = (E_0 - R)$. Similarly for the absorption process in another atom, for resonance absorption to occur the incident photon must have energy $E'_\gamma = (E_0 + R)$. In general, because of the Doppler effect due to thermal motion, broad emission and absorption spectra occur centred on E_γ and E'_γ, as shown in Figure 7.5. Because of the relatively small overlap of the two spectra very little resonance absorption is expected. Since increasing the temperature spreads the Doppler broadening there should be a gentle increase in absorption with rising temperature. Prior to the discovery of the Mössbauer effect nuclear resonance absorption had been observed only marginally, and with difficulty.

Mössbauer found unexpectedly that in some cases reducing the temperature produced a marked increase in the resonance absorption. When the source was given a small additional Doppler velocity (about $1 \, \text{cm} \, \text{sec}^{-1}$) with respect to the absorber, sharp peaks could be traced out. These were centred on the resonance energy E_0 and had the natural linewidth of the nuclear transition. $\Delta\nu/\nu$ was of the order of 10^{-12} (ν is the frequency of the gamma ray). This technique of applying small Doppler velocities and

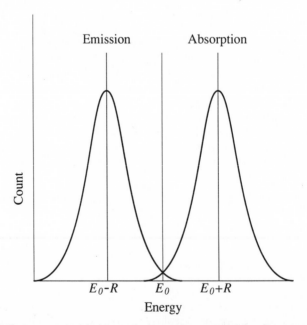

Figure 7.5 Gamma-ray emission and absorption spectra for free atoms, showing the displacements due to recoil and the small overlap.

investigating the resulting velocity spectrum has now become standard.

The reason for the Mössbauer effect is that recoilless emission and absorption of gamma rays can occur. In a solid, each atom is confined by its neighbours and at low temperatures the recoil momentum is taken up by the crystal as a whole, without emission or absorption of phonons (quantized lattice vibrations). Since the mass of the crystal is effectively infinite (compared with the mass of one atom) the recoil energy will be very small. Once recoilless emission and absorption can occur large resonance absorption is possible. Since the lines are so sharp they can be traced out by applying small energy displacements between source and absorber. This is done by imposing small changes in the relative velocity between them, using the Doppler effect. A typical absorption curve for a single nuclear transition is shown in Figure 7.6.

Because of its extreme resolution the Mössbauer effect makes possible the analysis of the hyperfine structure of nuclear transitions, and in particular the observation of the nuclear Zeeman effect. This permits the measurement of the fields causing the Zeeman splitting.

The magnetic moment of the nucleus can interact with an externally applied magnetic field or with unpaired electrons on its own atom and on its neighbours. The magnetic interaction with electrons is of two types. For s-electrons it is a contact interaction proportional to the electron density of the unpaired electrons at the nucleus, and for other electrons it is a dipole–dipole interaction.

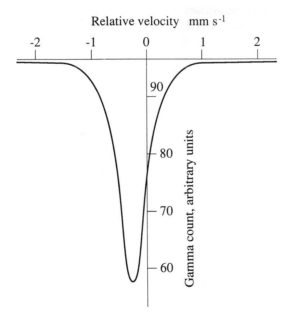

Figure 7.6 Experimental Mössbauer spectrum with an absorber of paramagnetic stainless steel. The displacement of the spectrum towards the left is the isomer shift (by courtesy of John Williams).

It is the innermost atomic electrons that contribute most to the contact interaction. A single 1s electron can produce an effective magnetic field at the nucleus of about 3×10^5 T (3×10^9 Oe). However, the 1s, 2s, 3s ... electrons usually exist predominantly in balanced pairs with equal numbers of opposite spins which tend to cancel out the interaction field. The interaction observed is usually due to the effect of unpaired outer s-electrons in the atoms, or is due to core polarization produced on the innermost s-electrons by external influences. Thus measurements on the nuclear Zeeman effect produced by these interactions lead to information either on the external influences producing core polarization, on unpaired outer s-electrons, or on dipole–dipole interactions.

The way that the measurements are interpreted may be seen by referring to the properties of the nucleus ^{57}Fe. This is a Mössbauer nucleus which is in common use, though not all nuclear species are suitable for observations on the Mössbauer effect.

Starting with nucleus ^{57}Co, this decays radioactively with a half-life of 270 days to an excited state of ^{57}Fe (Fig. 7.7) having a nuclear spin quantum number $I = 5/2$. This falls to its ground state ($I = 1/2$) either directly (9 per cent) or via the intermediate state (91 per cent) which has $I = 3/2$. The $I = 3/2$ state has an energy of 14·4 keV above the ground state and a lifetime $\tau = 1·4 \times 10^{-7}$ second.

The transition between $I = 3/2$ and $I = 1/2$ is used here. When there is no magnetic field or electric field gradient present the transition is of a single energy since the two levels are degenerate, producing the single Mössbauer line of Figure 7.6. In a magnetic field both levels split by an amount that is proportional to the field (Fig. 7.8). The selection rule for the

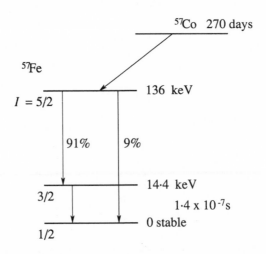

Figure 7.7 Decay scheme for ^{57}Fe.

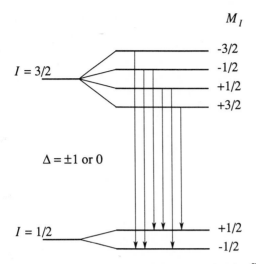

Figure 7.8 Scheme of energy level splitting for ^{57}Fe.

transition is that $\Delta m_I = \pm 1$ or 0, leading in this case to six different transition energies and six lines in the Zeeman spectrum (Fig. 7.9).

From the positions of the lines the splitting of the levels may be evaluated, and hence the strength of the effective magnetic field. Nuclear

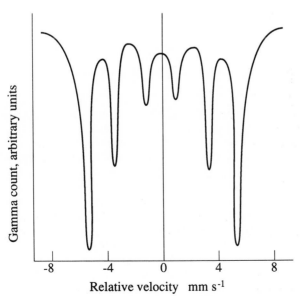

Figure 7.9 Experimental six-line Mössbauer absorption spectrum for ^{57}Fe contained in a ferromagnet (by courtesy of John Williams).

quadrupole interaction is effective when the nuclear charge is not spherically symmetrical. Then the presence of an electric field gradient can split the energy levels. This is not primarily relevant to magnetism and it will not be discussed here any more.

The isomer shift arises from the electrostatic interaction between the nuclear charge and the electronic charge within the volume of the nucleus. Only s-electrons are involved since only they have a finite probability density at the nucleus. The binding energy of an s-electron is changed depending on the volume occupied by the nuclear charge. The ground state and the excited states of the nucleus have slightly different charge radii. This has the effect of moving the whole Mössbauer pattern sideways to a different energy. The isomer shift is used to measure the difference in s-electron density at the nucleus between different environmental states of the same kind of atom.

Figure 7.10 illustrates how the Mössbauer hyperfine field in iron relates to the magnetization. Indeed the hyperfine field is closely related to the average spontaneous magnetization of the whole specimen. A typical hyperfine field is 30 T (3×10^5 Oe).

7.2.2 Nuclear magnetic resonance (NMR)

When a nucleus having a nuclear magnetic moment μ_N and total angular momentum $Ih/2\pi$ is placed in a magnetic field B_0 it has magnetic energy

$$E_m = -\mu_N B_0$$

An equal splitting of the $(2I+1)$ sub-levels is produced. The energy separation between adjacent sub-levels is

$$\Delta E = g_I B_0 h/2\pi$$

where g_I is the nuclear g-factor. There can be resonance absorption of electromagnetic radiation of frequency ν (angular frequency ω) where

$$\nu = \Delta E/h \text{ or } \omega = 2\pi/h\Delta E$$

The field B_0 would usually be made up of contributions from an externally applied field and a hyperfine field B_H.

The resonant absorption may be observed in a number of ways. One method is to place a sample of the material being investigated in a tank circuit tuned to a particular frequency, and to apply a slowly varying magnetic field. Resonance is detected from the characteristics of the electronic circuit in which the cavity is placed. The applied field at resonance is measured and the hyperfine field is thus derived. Other methods involve fixing the field and looking for a resonant frequency. Not all nuclear species are suitable for NMR studies.

The hyperfine field measured by NMR is exactly the same as that measured for the same nuclear species from the Mössbauer effect. However, a nucleus suitable for Mössbauer studies is not necessarily suitable for NMR studies, and *vice versa*. Thus NMR nuclei may also be used as sensitive probes of magnetic interaction fields in solids. One

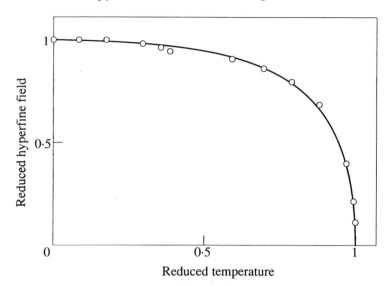

Figure 7.10 Experimental reduced temperature dependence of the hyperfine field in ferromagnetic iron (circles). The full line shows the spontaneous magnetization derived from bulk magnetic measurements (from Preston et al., 1962, *Phys. Rev.*, **128**, 2207).

application is to compare the resonance measured in a metallic specimen being investigated with that measured for another non-metallic specimen containing the same NMR nuclei in as nearly as possible the same environment except for the absence of the metallic state. The displacement in the resonant frequency is called the Knight shift. It is due to the overlap with the nucleus of s-conduction electrons polarized by the applied magnetic field. It gives a measure of the properties of s-electrons near the Fermi level in the metal.

7.2.3 Nuclear contribution to the specific heat capacity

As we have seen already, when a nucleus with angular momentum quantum number I is acted upon by a magnetic field, $(2I + 1)$ sub-levels all having different energies are produced. At high temperatures these are all filled statistically as dictated by the thermal energy available. When the temperature is reduced to a low level there is a redistribution among the energy levels and the energy associated with the redistribution shows up as a contribution c_N of Schottky type (Fig. 7.11) to the total specific heat capacity. This gives information on the energy spacing of the sub-levels and hence on the magnitude of the hyperfine field giving rise to the splitting of levels. The nuclear heat capacity c_N has its maximum at that temperature T_m at which

$$kT_m \simeq \mu_N B_H / I$$

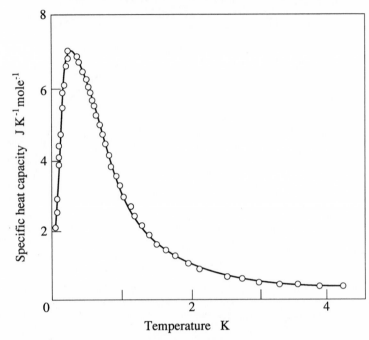

Figure 7.11 The specific heat capacity of holmium at low temperatures, showing the nuclear contribution (from van Kempen, Miedema and Huiskamp, 1964, *Physica*, **30**, 229).

Because of the smallness of nuclear magnetic moments this is usually at temperatures of the order of 10 mK to 100 mK.

Among other experiments not discussed here that give information on hyperfine interactions are electron spin resonance and the scattering of polarized neutrons.

Chapter 8 ⎯⎯⎯⎯⎯⎯⎯

Domain magnetism

8.1 Basic principles

A ferromagnetic specimen made of a material such as iron may be demagnetized by putting it into an alternating field of suitably decreasing amplitude. Starting with the demagnetized state and applying an increasing unidirectional field the magnetization increases, slowly and reversibly at first, but thereafter quickly and irreversibly, then finally slowly until eventually the saturated state is reached. In some ferromagnets magnetic saturation occurs in weak fields as low as 10^{-6} T (10^{-2} Oe), and yet the magnetization of the same specimen can be zero in zero field. These apparently contradictory observations are very significant.

It is known from the study of paramagnetism that applying a small field has an entirely negligible effect on the magnetization of a system of free and independent elementary magnetic moments. This difficulty is overcome by assuming that each domain is intrinsically fully magnetized under the influence of exchange interactions described by a molecular field. Changes in overall magnetization in relatively low fields are almost all due to rearrangements of domains and the boundaries between them. The physical nature of the domain boundaries is of great interest, as are the mechanisms that control boundary movements. The demagnetized state is where the overall magnetization of the collection of separate domains cancels out because they are all orientated differently.

The reason for the formation of the domain structure is that the potential energy associated with the magnetized sample is thereby minimized. This is in spite of the cost in energy of forming the domain boundaries.

Studies of domain properties in ferromagnets tend to be on the properties of either soft or hard magnetic materials. The technological aim of such work is to improve soft materials by making it possible for domain boundaries to sweep through the solid with the minimum constraint. In hard materials the usual aim is to lock the magnetized state into position as permanently as possible.

Technical applications of domain properties are described more fully in Chapter 9. The range of coercivities found experimentally is from about 2×10^{-7} T (2×10^{-3} Oe) in the best transformer alloys to about 1 T (10^4 Oe) in high-stability, high-performance magnets.

8.1.1 Magnetocrystalline anisotropy

Crystal orientation is important when domain properties are considered. Due to magnetocrystalline anisotropy differing energies are involved in magnetizing a specimen in different crystallographic directions. Much of the earlier part of the discussion here refers to the properties of single crystals having selected orientations. In polycrystalline specimens there is usually a randomly oriented array of small crystallites. Sometimes a magnetic material is heterogeneous, consisting of islands of a strongly magnetized phase, which is randomly oriented, embedded in a matrix of a weakly magnetized or non-ferromagnetic phase.

The potential energy of a single crystal sample of a ferromagnet depends on the direction with respect to the crystal axes in which it is magnetized. The energy is lowest in an easy direction and a higher field must be applied to make the magnetization lie in a harder direction. This is illustrated for iron, cobalt and nickel in Figure 1.4.

Hexagonal cobalt is uniaxial, having only a single easy direction along the hexagonal axis. The magnetocrystalline energy E_k of a uniaxial ferromagnet is written empirically as a series

$$E_k = K_1 \sin^2\theta + K_2 \sin^4\theta + \ldots = \sum K_n \sin^{2n}\theta \qquad (8.1)$$

where $K_1, K_2 \ldots$ are empirical constants which vary with temperature and which differ for different materials. θ is the angle between the magnetization vector and the direction of the crystallographic axis. Odd powers of $\sin\theta$ do not appear because the series must be symmetrical with respect to either direction along the easy axis.

In iron any of the three cube edge directions are directions of easy magnetization. The energy of a cubic crystal may be written

$$E_k = K_0 + K_1(\alpha_1^2\alpha_2^2 + \alpha_1^2\alpha_3^2 + \alpha_2^2\alpha_3^2) + K_2(\alpha_1^2\alpha_2^2\alpha_3^2) + \ldots \qquad (8.2)$$

where $\alpha_1, \alpha_2, \alpha_3$ are the direction cosines of the magnetization direction with respect to the cubic axes of the crystal.

In each case the series is short, the magnitude of the anisotropy constant K_n decreasing rapidly with increasing n and becoming lost in experimental error.

In cubic crystals the easy directions are along the cube edges if K_1 is positive and K_2 is not more negative than $-9/4K_1$. When K_1 is negative, as for nickel, the easy directions are along the cube diagonals.

The order of magnitude of the magnetocrystalline energies involved is given by the values of K_1 for different materials (at room temperature) shown in Table 8.1.

The effect of this energy on the domain structure is that it imposes a constraint on the direction that the magnetization takes up in a given crystal when no external field is applied. And it also makes an important contribution to the intrinsic energy of domain boundary walls and controls their thickness.

In materials in which the magnetism comes from atoms and ions of the first transition series the magnetic moments are due to spin moments,

Table 8.1 First anisotropy constants K_1

Material	K_1 (J m^{-3})	K_1 (erg cm^{-3})
Fe	4.7×10^4	4.7×10^5
Co	4.1×10^5	4.1×10^6
Ni	5.1×10^3	5.1×10^4
SmCo$_5$	1.1×10^7	1.1×10^8

mainly of 3d electrons, and these are not coupled directly with the crystal lattice. Here the magnetic anisotropy energy arises from the indirect coupling of the spins with the lattice via the spin–orbit coupling and the orbit–lattice coupling. The extent to which a magnetic ion feels the symmetry of the lattice depends strongly and in a fairly complicated way on its electronic structure and a wide variety of cases occurs.

Where the source of the magnetism is atoms and ions of the rare earths the magnetic moments consist of both orbital and spin moments. Here there is a direct coupling between orbital moment and lattice and the resultant magnetic anistropy is usually much stronger than for the indirectly coupled transition series materials.

8.1.2 Magnetostatic energy

When a ferromagnetic body is isolated and placed in a saturating field B_0 free magnetic poles appear to be located on its end surfaces. The effect is produced by the normal component of magnetization being discontinuous at the surfaces, or where the magnetization is internally non-uniform. The field $(B_0)_i$ acting inside the body may be written

$$(B_0)_i = B_0 - (B_0)_D \tag{8.3}$$

where $(B_0)_D$ is the demagnetizating field. It is that which would be produced by the apparent surface pole distribution acting in isolation.

The demagnetizing field applies to all magnetized materials, even weak paramagnets, although sometimes its effect is small. Its magnitude depends on the shape of the specimen and on the magnetization M. The demagnetizing factor D is defined by

$$(B_0)_D = DM \tag{8.4}$$

D has been tabulated for ellipsoids of revolution, for which the calculation is exact (Fig. 8.1). D may be calculated approximately for other figures. Rectangular rods of square cross section have values of D close to those for ellipsoids having the same ratio of length l to breadth b. For $l/b > 1$, D is roughly proportional to $(l/b)^{-1}$. When the specimen is longer and thinner, the demagnetizing field is smaller.

The magnetostatic energy E_m per unit volume of the body when it is in an external field B_0 is the sum of two terms depending respectively on the internal and the external fields.

$$E_m = -1/2(B_0)_i M - B_0 M \tag{8.5}$$

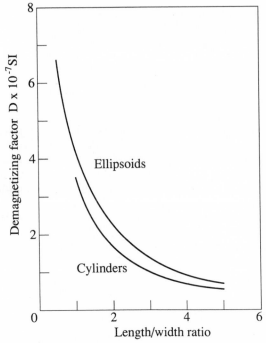

Figure 8.1 Demagnetizing factors for ellipsoids and cylinders.

When no field is applied externally only the demagnetizing field of the uniformly magnetized specimen remains. The self energy is then

$$E_s = 1/2DM^2 \qquad (8.6)$$

The factor 1/2 arises because if it were omitted mutual interactions within the solid would be counted twice. The mutual energy of two dipoles is given by the product of one dipole moment and the field due to the other.

This self energy is relatively large and the domain structure which occurs naturally is that which minimizes it. A uniformly magnetized (single domain) ellipsoid of iron having a length/breadth ratio of 3·0 would have a self energy of about $1·7 \times 10^5$ J m^{-3} ($1·7 \times 10^6$ erg cm^{-3}).

In a rectangular body magnetized along its length (Fig. 8.2), changing from a single domain to two equal oppositely magnetized domains reduces the self energy to about one half. This is because the ratio of length to breadth of each domain is doubled and in consequence the demagnetizing field is approximately halved. This reduction in energy through domains narrowing cannot continue indefinitely because it must be set against the increase in energy due to the necessary creation of new domain boundaries.

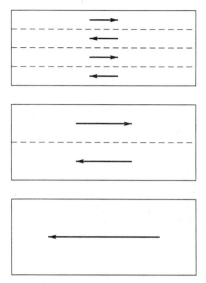

Figure 8.2 Division of a rectangular ferromagnetic block into parallel domains. The lengths of the arrows indicate the magnitude of the demagnetizing field.

8.1.3 Domain boundary walls (Bloch walls)

A domain boundary wall (Fig. 8.3) consists of the transition layer which separates adjacent domains magnetized in different directions. The total angular displacement across a wall is commonly 180 degrees or 90 degrees. The whole change in spin direction does not usually occur in one discontinuous jump at a single atomic plane but it takes place gradually over many planes. What determines the thickness (width) of a wall is a compromise between the opposing influences of exchange energy and magnetocrystalline anisotropy energy.

Following Equation (7.1) the increase in exchange energy between two spins displaced through a small angle ϕ from their equilibrium parallel alignment is

$$\Delta E_{ex} = J S^2 \phi^2 \tag{8.7}$$

where J is the exchange integral and S is the spin quantum number. If the total angular displacement across the wall is ϕ_0, made in N steps over a line of $N+1$ atoms, the total energy of the line is

$$\Delta E_{ex} = J S^2 \phi_0^2 / N \tag{8.8}$$

Thus the exchange energy of a line of atoms perpendicular to the wall is inversely proportional to the number of steps in the line. A wall 101 atomic layers thick has exchange energy only 1/100 of the energy of a wall in which all the angular change is between two neighbours. The thicker the wall, the cheaper it is in exchange energy.

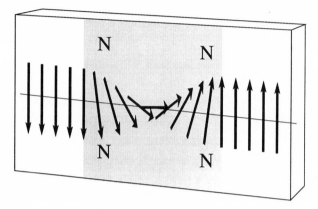

Figure 8.3 Domain boundary wall (after Kittel, 1949, *Rev. Mod. Phys.*, **21**, 561).

The thickness and the energy of a domain wall may be estimated for particular cases. One important case which we consider here is that of a wall parallel to a (001) plane in iron, which separates domains magnetized in opposite directions. The directions of the magnetization of the adjacent domains are taken as [100] (x direction) and [1̄00] (−x direction). The z direction is normal to the domain wall.

The rotation of the spin direction on passing through the wall is such that the spin always lies in the plane of the wall, because the normal component of the magnetization must remain constant through the wall. This follows from the condition for minimum magnetostatic energy, with no extra free poles being formed.

Let θ be the angle between the spin direction and the x-axis. Thus θ varies from 0 to π (= 180 degrees). The angle-dependent magnetocrystalline anisotropy energy density in the (x,y) plane is then (from Equation (8.2)).

$E_k = K_1(\alpha_1^2\alpha_2^2 + \alpha_1^2\alpha_3^2 + \alpha_2^2\alpha_3^2)$, omitting the K_2 term, which is zero when $\alpha_3 = 0$. Here $\alpha_1 = \cos\theta$; $\alpha_2 = \sin\theta$; $\alpha_3 = 0$, so

$$E_k = K_1 \sin^2\theta \cos^2\theta \qquad (8.9)$$

The exchange energy (non-uniformity energy) can be estimated similarly. We consider two neighbouring lattice points denoted by the position vectors r_i and r_j, their separation being r_{ij}. Let the direction cosines of the spin direction of the atom at r_j be α_j^x, α_j^y, α_j^z. Now the direction cosines α_i^x, α_i^y, α_i^z of the spin at r_i may be expanded in a Taylor series

$$\alpha_i^x = \alpha_j^x + [x_{ij}(\partial/\partial x_{ij}) + y_{ij}(\partial/\partial y_{ij}) + z_{ij}(\partial/\partial z_{ij})]\alpha_j^x$$
$$+ 1/2[x_{ij}^2(\partial^2/\partial x_{ij}^2) + y_{ij}^2(\partial^2/\partial y_{ij}^2) + z_{ij}^2(\partial^2/\partial z_{ij}^2)]\alpha_j^x + \ldots,$$
and so on. $\qquad (8.10)$

Equations (8.10) may be summed over nearest neighbours for the body-centred cubic lattice (of lattice parameter a) that is under consideration; and simplified to take account of the two atoms per unit cell. The result for the exchange energy density becomes

$$E_{ex} = (2J S^2/a)[(\nabla \alpha_1)^2 + (\nabla \alpha_2)^2 + (\nabla \alpha_3)^2] \qquad (8.11)$$

In the present case, since $\alpha_1 = \cos \theta$; $\alpha_2 = \sin \theta$; $\alpha_3 = 0$ we have

$$E_{ex} = A(d\theta/dz)^2 \qquad (8.12)$$

where $A = 2J S^2/a$

Because the exchange theory is inexact various supposedly self-consistent experimental parameters lead to different values for A. The value derived from the low temperature dependence of magnetization on temperature is related to spin wave theory, which is itself closely allied to the behaviour of domain boundary walls. For iron this leads to a value of the exchange interaction parameter $J = 205 \, k$, where k is the Boltzmann constant. If we assume $S = 1$ (two spins per atom) and putting $a = 2.86$ Å (0.286 nm) we obtain

$$A = 2J S^2/a \approx 2 \times 10^{-11} \, \text{J m}^{-1} \, (= 2 \times 10^{-6} \, \text{erg cm}^{-1})$$

The total wall energy per unit area, E_{wall}, is the sum of the energies given by Equations (8.9) and (8.12), integrated over the whole wall.

$$E_{wall} = \int_{-\infty}^{+\infty} (K_1 \sin^2 \theta \cos^2 \theta + A(d\theta/dz)^2) \, dz \qquad (8.13)$$

In Equation (8.13), θ is to be determined as that function of z which minimizes the total energy. The full derivation is not given here, but an important intermediate result is that for all values of z

$$K_1 \sin^2 \theta \cos^2 \theta = A(d\theta/dz)^2 \qquad (8.14)$$

This shows that at every point of the domain wall the local anisotropy energy density is equal to the local exchange energy density. In directions of high anisotropy energy, neighbouring spins make larger angles with each other than in directions of low anisotropy energy.

The solution is of the form

$$\cos \theta = \tanh(z(K_1/A)^{1/2}) \qquad (8.15)$$

where z is measured from the centre of the wall. This is illustrated in Figure 8.4.

From Equation (8.14)

$$dz = (A/K_1)^{1/2} \frac{d\theta}{\sin \theta \cos \theta} \qquad (8.16)$$

Substituting for dz and $d\theta/dz$ in Equation (8.13) gives for the wall energy (per unit area)

$$E_{wall} = 2(K_1 A)^{1/2} \int_0^{\pi} |\sin \theta \cos \theta| \, d\theta = 2(K_1 A)^{1/2} \qquad (8.17)$$

Thus the wall energy for iron at room temperature is of the order of

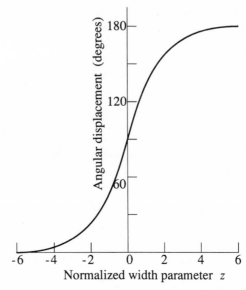

Figure 8.4 Angular distribution of spins in a 180° domain boundary wall.

$$2 \times (2 \times 10^{-11} \times 4 \cdot 7 \times 10^4)^{1/2} = 1 \cdot 94 \times 10^{-3}\,\text{J m}^{-2}\ (= 1 \cdot 94\,\text{erg cm}^{-2})$$

The order of magnitude of the thickness of the domain boundary wall is

$$\delta \simeq \pi (A/K_1)^{1/2} \tag{8.18}$$

The factor $(A/K_1)^{1/2} = \delta_1$ is often referred to as the domain wall thickness parameter.

Using the same values for A and K_1 gives

$$\delta = \pi \left[\frac{2 \times 10^{-11}}{4 \cdot 7 \times 10^4} \right]^{1/2} = 6 \cdot 5 \times 10^{-8}\,\text{m}\ (= 65\,\text{nm} = 650\,\text{Å})$$

These values for wall energy and thickness compare reasonably well with what is found experimentally.

8.2 Arrangements of domains

The shape and size of the domains present in equilibrium in a specimen are given by the condition that the total energy shall be a minimum. They depend considerably on the actual configuration of the specimen.

In a long, thin single crystal of iron cut with its surface accurately parallel to a (100) crystal face, the domain boundaries are parallel lines and the domains which they separate are alternately oppositely magnetized in the direction of the lines. At the end surfaces domains of closure are formed. These minimize the formation of free poles and reduce the magnetostatic energy. But extra domain boundaries need to be created (Fig. 8.5), which cost energy.

When a field is applied to such a specimen along its length the boundary walls move laterally so that those domains magnetized in the same sense as the field grow wider and those magnetized in the opposite sense contract. Other orientations are more complicated. Figure 8.6 shows what happens with a rectangular single crystal of iron cut with its (110) direction along its long axis, when a field is applied along the (110) direction. The top face is perpendicular to the (100) direction. Ninety-degree domain walls predominate and closure domains are formed which contain the flux within the ferromagnet and minimize the magnetostatic energy.

When the surface of the specimen is even very slightly inclined to a (100) face of an iron crystal, a 'fir tree' pattern grows around the lines of the longitudinal domain boundaries (Fig. 8.7) and this gets more prominent as the inclination increases. The tree patterns are a kind of closure domain (Fig. 8.8).

8.2.1 Experimental observation of magnetic domains

The long-established method of looking at magnetic domains is by using Bitter patterns. A magnetic colloid, or fine particles of a magnetic powder, is spread on the surface of the specimen being examined. The surface must be carefully polished electrolytically and must be free from strains. The particles are attracted to regions of strong magnetic field gradient, where domain boundaries intersect the surface. Suitable magnetic colloids are easy to make and use but to prepare a suitably strain-free polished surface

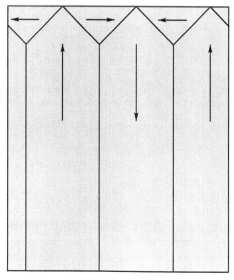

Figure 8.5 Domains of closure.

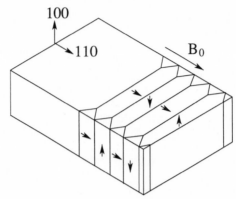

Figure 8.6 Domain structure in a single crystal specimen of iron when the field and the magnetization are along a [100] direction (after Stoner, 1950, *Rep. Prog. Phys.*, **13**, 114).

Figure 8.7 Tracing of an experimental Bitter pattern showing fir-tree domains on the surface of an iron–silicon alloy single crystal cut nearly parallel to a (100) crystal face. The magnification of the picture is about 500 times (after Williams, Bozorth and Shockley, 1949, *Phys. Rev.*, **75**, 155).

that characterizes the whole specimen is difficult. The method has been used extensively for the study of static domain structures at room temperature but for dynamic studies of domain wall movements and for temperatures different from room temperature it cannot really be used.

Another method uses the magneto-optic Kerr effect. The polarization state of light reflected from a magnetized surface depends on the direction and magnitude of the magnetization of the reflecting surface. Sensitive methods for the polarization analysis are required since the magnitude of the Kerr rotation is only of the order of one or two minutes of arc.

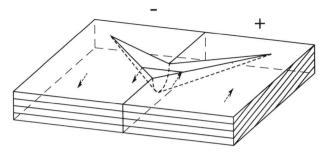

Figure 8.8 Interpretation of tree patterns. The side face shows end traces of (100) planes (from Stoner, loc cit).

With transparent magnetic specimens such as garnets the Faraday effect may be used. The rotation of the plane of polarization of light transmitted through the specimen depends on the domain arrangement and the magnetization. A suitable analysing microscope allows observation of the domain structure right through the volume of a thin specimen. Magneto-optic methods are available for dynamic studies of domains, even in oscillatory fields of fairly high frequency. Also a much wider range of sample temperature is possible than with Bitter patterns.

Another method for examining domain structure and behaviour uses transmission electron microscopy (Lorentz microscopy). Specimens have the form of thin films $1/10\,\mu m$ thick or less and the electron beam is transmitted through, as shown in Figure 8.9. The beam is deviated according to the magnetization of the regions it passes through and the pattern reaching a suitably placed detector reveals sensitive information about the domain structure.

8.2.2 Magneto-elastic energy and magnetostriction

The magnetostrictive effect is the change in dimensions which accompanies a change in the magnetization of a ferromagnet. The magnetostriction coefficient λ is the fractional change in length associated with a change in magnetization from zero to the saturation value. Magnetostriction differs in different crystallographic directions in the ferromagnetic single crystal.

The effect of a unidirectional strain in a specimen is to introduce an additional anisotropy in the magnetization. In iron, for example, the effect of tension is to produce a tendency towards a preferred direction of magnetization parallel to the direction of the strain. There is an associated magneto-elastic energy.

A close physical relationship exists between the magnetocrystalline anisotropy and the magnetostriction. Magnetostriction occurs because the magnetocrystalline anisotropy energy depends on the strain in such a way that the stable state of the crystal is deformed with respect to the original lattice. The crystal will deform spontaneously if to do so will lower the magnetocrystalline anisotropy energy.

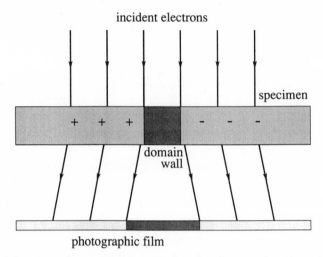

Figure 8.9 Lorentz electron microscopy for showing up domain walls in thin samples.

Magneto-elastic energies can make an important contribution to the total magnetic energy of a ferromagnetic crystal which is strained, and so they can affect the domain properties very significantly. It is this aspect which most concerns us here. We simplify the treatment by assuming that the magneto-elastic effects act as though they give rise to an apparent contribution to the magnetocrystalline anisotropy of the crystal.

An isotropic magnetostriction coefficient λ is defined, being some weighted mean of the directional coefficients (for cubic crystals) λ_{100} and λ_{111}. The magneto-elastic contribution to the energy is then

$$E_{me} = 3/2\lambda\tau \sin^2\phi \qquad (8.19)$$

where τ is the tensile stress acting and ϕ is the angle between this stress and the direction of the magnetization.

As a result, domain walls are expected to encounter local energy barriers due to stresses in the vicinity of imperfections in crystals.

8.2.3 Magnetization curves and domain wall equilibrium

When a 180° domain boundary wall of area A moves laterally through a displacement x, a volume Ax of the specimen reverses its magnetization, from $+M$ to $-M$. The associated change in magnetic energy per unit area of the wall is then

$$2(B_0)_i Mx$$

where $(B_0)_i$ is the internal field acting. If E is the potential energy per unit area of the boundary (related to its existence but not necessarily localized in the boundary itself), the condition for equilibrium in a field B_0 is

$$d/dx(E - 2B_0Mx) = 0 \qquad (8.20)$$

x is so defined that $x = 0$ at a position of equilibrium. That is,

$$2B_0 M = dE/dx \qquad (8.21)$$

It is expected that E will be a randomly varying function of position (Fig. 8.10) due to the effect of local strains and other crystal imperfections on the boundary wall. As the field increases slowly, the boundary moves at first reversibly and the magnetization is a reversible function of the field. Eventually dE/dx reaches a maximum value at b where the equilibrium becomes unstable. When the corresponding value of the field

$$(B_0)_{crit} = (dE/dx)_{max}/2M \qquad (8.22)$$

has been passed the boundary moves spontaneously, with discontinuous and irreversible increase in magnetization, to a new position of equilibrium c having the same value of dE/dx. With further increase of field reversible movement of the boundary is resumed until a new maximum in dE/dx is reached and further irreversible movement takes place. Eventually the field is large enough to sweep all boundaries through the specimen. Thereafter, in this particular example, the specimen is saturated. Otherwise when domains are present the magnetization of which does not lie in the field direction, the approach to saturation proceeds by a process of magnetization rotation.

If from position c in Figure 8.10 the field is reduced, the sign of the

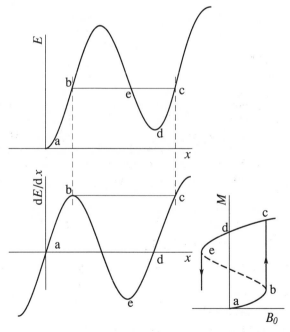

Figure 8.10 Diagrams illustrating reversible and irreversible domain boundary movements (after Stoner and Rhodes, 1949, *Phil. Mag.*, **40**, 481).

change in the magnetization energy in Equation (8.20) is reversed and the discontinuous jump (in the reverse direction) cannot occur until the minimum in dE/dx at e is reached. The graph of magnetization against field shows hysteresis and the observation of a hysteresis loop (Fig. 1.1) is explained.

Where the domain walls are more strongly pinned into deeper energy minima, sweeping out the walls is a more difficult process and we get a harder ferromagnet and a wider hysteresis loop.

For a macroscopic specimen the overall behaviour of all the domain walls present is compounded, smoothing out the discontinuous nature of the magnetization changes. However, with a suitable detecting system discontinuous very small jumps in magnetization can be observed in that part of the hysteresis loop which is irreversible. This is the Barkhausen effect.

The coercivity of the material is closely related to the influences which pin the domain walls in position, making them difficult to move under the influence of applied fields.

8.3 Single domain particles

When the physical size of a magnetized body is made smaller the relative contribution of the domain boundary energy to the total energy increases. Eventually a point is reached where it is energetically unfavourable for a domain boundary to be formed. The specimen then behaves as a single domain and its properties differ from the properties when domain walls are present. Such a situation can occur in heterogeneous magnetic alloys in which fine particles of a ferromagnetic phase are dispersed within a non-ferromagnetic or a much less strongly ferromagnetic matrix.

To see what properties are expected to be associated with single domain particles we consider the simplest case, that of a single prolate ellipsoid, having directions of magnetization and applied field as shown in Figure 8.11. Initially only magnetic anisotropy due to shape (magnetostatic energy) is considered, without magnetocrystalline and magneto-elastic effects. It turns out in the end that the effects left out can be treated in exactly the same way as shape anisotropy and they produce the same results.

The general expression for the self energy associated with the demagnetizing field (compare Equation (8.6)) of a general ellipsoid is

$$E_s = 1/2M^2(D_1\alpha_1^2 + D_2\alpha_2^2 + D_3\alpha_3^2) \tag{8.23}$$

where α_1, α_2, α_3 are the direction cosines of the magnetization M with respect to the principal axes of the ellipsoid and D_1, D_2, D_3 are the demagnetization coefficients along these axes.

In the present case this becomes

$$E_s = 1/2M^2(D_a \cos^2\psi + D_b \sin^2\psi) \tag{8.24}$$

where a and b refer to the polar and equatorial axes respectively. The

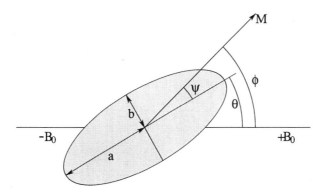

Figure 8.11 Definition of parameters for a prolate ellipsoid in a magnetic field.

energy associated with the field applied externally (see Equation (8.5)) is

$$E_{B_0} = -B_0 M \cos \phi \qquad (8.25)$$

The total relevant energy is now

$$E' = E_s + E_{B_0}$$
$$= 1/4(D_b + D_a)M^2 - 1/4(D_b - D_a)M^2 \cos 2\psi - B_0 M \cos \phi \quad (8.26)$$

Equation (8.26) may be expressed in a dimensionless form

$$\eta' = \frac{E'}{(D_b - D_a)M^2} = \frac{1}{4} \cdot \left(\frac{D_b + D_a}{D_b - D_a} \right)$$

$$- \frac{\cos 2\psi}{4} - \frac{B_0}{(D_b - D_a)M} \cos \phi \qquad (8.27)$$

or, for the variable part of the energy

$$\eta = -1/4 \cos 2\psi - b \cos \phi \qquad (8.28)$$
$$= -1/4 \cos 2(\phi - \theta) - b \cos \phi \qquad (8.29)$$

where $b = B_0/(D_b - D_a)M$ is a reduced field. Treating b and θ as fixed, the stationary (equilibrium) values of Equation (8.29) are given by

$$\partial \eta / \partial \phi = 1/2 \sin 2(\phi - \theta) + b \sin \phi = 0 \qquad (8.30)$$

Solutions of Equation (8.30) are required which give equilibrium values for $\cos \phi$ over a range of values for b and at different values of the orientation angle θ. Cos ϕ is really a reduced magnetization in the field direction while b is the reduced field.

Graphs of solutions for different values of θ are given in Figure 8.12. The combination of results for a collection of randomly oriented prolate ellipsoids of fixed ellipticity gives the graph shown in Figure 8.13.

If the anisotropy of the particles is entirely due to shape the maximum reduced coercivity b_c is where $b_c = 1$ (Fig. 8.12), for particles whose major

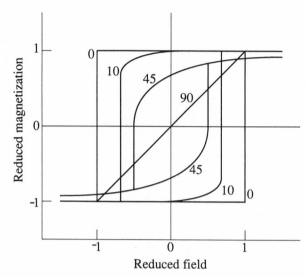

Figure 8.12 Calculated magnetization curves for uniformly magnetized prolate ellipsoids. The numbers on the curves are values for θ, as defined in Figure 8.11 (after Stoner and Wohlfarth, 1948, *Phil. Trans. Roy Soc.*, **A240**, 599).

axis lies in the same direction as the field. For randomly oriented particles $(b_c)_{ave} = 0.479$.

The upper limit of $(D_b - D_a)$ for long thin particles is $2\pi \times 10^{-7}$ SI units (2π cgs units). Thus the highest possible coercivity due entirely to shape anisotropy in single domain particles is $(B_0)_c = 2\pi \times 10^{-7} M$ teslas $(= 2\pi I$ oersteds). This gives maximum coercive field values of about $1.1, 0.3, 0.9$ T for iron, nickel and cobalt respectively (11 000, 3 000, 9 000 Oe). These maxima are not reached experimentally.

The basic treatment outlined here is for shape anisotropy. Exactly the same solution is obtained for spherical particles subject to stress. The difference lies in the definition of the reduced field, which becomes $b = B_0 M / 3\lambda\tau$ where λ is the effective magnetostriction coefficient and τ is the stress. Magneto-elastic effects in single-domain particles are insufficient to account for the observed high coercivities in hard magnetic materials. The internal stresses required to make such an explanation fit the experimental data are greater than the elastic limits of the materials concerned, and therefore this part of the theory is unsatisfactory.

For iron, nickel and cobalt the highest coercivities expected from stress alone are 0.06 T, 0.4 T and 0.06 T (600, 4 000, 600 Oe) respectively.

The treatment is also the same for magnetocrystalline anisotropy, the reduced field becoming

$$b = B_0 M / 2K_1$$

This leads to expected maximum coercivities due to magnetocrystalline anisotropy for iron, nickel and cobalt of about $0.05, 0.02$ and 0.6 T (500, 200 and 6 000 Oe).

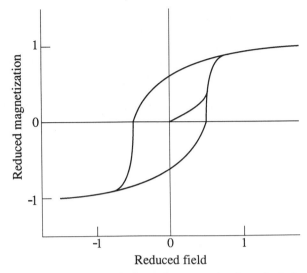

Figure 8.13 Calculated hysteresis loop for a randomly oriented collection of prolate ellipsoids of fixed ellipticity (after Stoner and Wohlfarth, loc cit).

Different mechanisms of domain magnetization are not really so clearly separable as might appear. In actual materials the boundaries between the regions of applicability of different mechanisms are diffuse. Often more than one mechanism operates at the same time. Such overlap would occur in a heterogeneous material containing particles of a range of sizes, some containing only one domain and others more than one.

This treatment is too simple because it is assumed that when the magnetization of a single-domain particle reverses it is by a mechanism of rotation of all the individual atomic magnetic moments in unison. This is not necessarily the case. Other, non-collinear, models (for instance 'buckling' and 'curling') have been proposed and their properties, while different, are likely to be equally valid.

8.3.1 Superparamagnetism

The single domain particles we have discussed so far are just small enough to show single domain behaviour. The actual diameter differs in different materials but typically it is of the order of one micrometre. Now we consider smaller particles.

Various experiments have shown that even at sizes so small that the particles contain only a few thousand atoms the intrinsic magnetization and the Curie temperature are essentially independent of particle size. However, the magnetization vector becomes unstable in this range of size and begins to wander in a thermally activated manner analogous to Brownian movement. The magnetic anisotropy energy of a particle is proportional to its volume. When the volume is small enough the magnetic energy of the particle approaches its thermal energy kT, and the magnetization vector fluctuates in the same way as in a classical paramagnetic gas. The available orientations are so close together as to appear continuous. Each particle contains many atoms, giving the classical condition for which the quantum number J has the value infinity, in the treatment of Section 2.3. This condition is called superparamagnetism.

The magnetic moment of one particle is $\mu = MV$, where V is its volume. The apparent magnetization M_a of an assembly of such particles in thermal equilibrium at a temperature T is given by adapting Equation (2.6), giving

$$M_a/M = \coth(\mu B_0/kT) - kT/\mu B_0 \qquad (8.31)$$

One feature of Equation (8.31) is that the apparent magnetization is determined universally by the ratio of field to temperature, B_0/T. This is found experimentally, as shown in Figure 8.14. When B_0/T is small, what

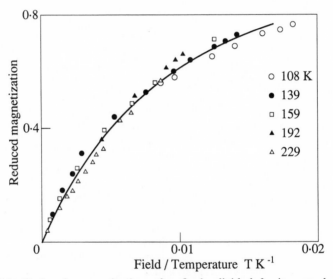

Figure 8.14 Reduced magnetization of a finely divided ferrite sample plotted against B_0/T for several different temperatures. The points are experimental. The line is calculated from the Brillouin function with $J = \infty$ and fitted to the experimental data at one point.

seems to be true paramagnetic behaviour occurs and Equation (8.31) can be approximated to its shortened form, as in Section 2.4. This gives

$$M_a/M = \mu B_0/3kT \qquad (8.32)$$

By using Equation (8.32), μ can be measured experimentally and hence the particle volume may be determined.

Since the apparent magnetization is zero when no external field is applied the coercivity associated with larger single domain particles disappears. Thus a reduction in the size of highly coercive single domain particles eventually produces a fall in coercivity.

We have been discussing the condition of thermal equilibrium so far. In fact significant relaxation times τ sometimes occur when the superparamagnetic region is being approached, these decreasing rapidly as the magnetic energy approaches kT. This is illustrated in Table 8.2.

Table 8.2 Relaxation times of single-domain particles

$\mu B_0/kT$	τ (sec)
50	5×10^{12}
25	10^2
18	10^{-1}
10	2×10^{-5}
1	3×10^{-9}

8.4 Soft magnetic materials

Soft ferromagnetic or ferrimagnetic materials are those which have been developed with technical applications in view, to allow changes in magnetization to occur easily in weak fields. In this chapter we deal with the materials themselves, deferring a discussion of applications to Chapter 9. Different groups of materials exist according to the particular physical property that is being exploited.

The first group is that having the highest possible permeability, usually under static conditions; that is, where the change in induction B produced by a small field B_0 is as large as possible. Here the requirement is to minimize the constraints on the mechanisms by which change of overall magnetization takes place. One approach is to make pure single crystal specimens that are chemically and structurally of a high degree of perfection. This has been possible in a few special cases, but it is not very attractive commercially. The other approach is to find materials with fundamental properties which minimize the effect of imperfections on the magnetism.

Some binary iron–nickel alloys have been developed in this way. Starting with pure nickel, iron can be added in solid solution over a wide range of composition. The structure remains face-centred cubic, with the iron and the nickel randomly distributed over the crystallographic sites. As this iron content increases, so does the magnetization, but the magnetization remains relatively low.

At the same time the first anisotropy constant K_1 (Section 8.1.1) varies from a negative value for low iron concentrations, through zero at about 25 per cent of iron and becomes positive as the iron concentration is increased further. Low values of K_1 (and also of K_2, which shows a similar dependence on composition) lead to low domain wall energies, easier domain wall motion and high permeability. Similarly it is desirable to reduce the effect of internal stresses in pinning domain walls by having a magnetostriction coefficient λ which is as small as possible. In these alloys

λ also passes through zero at nearly the same composition, though a few per cent nearer the nickel-rich side. Thus by careful choice of composition and accepting a small compromise the permeability can be made greatest. Various commercial alloys exist having different trade names where small amounts of third elements are added in order to optimize the properties.

A further complication is that there is a tendency to form a crystallographic superlattice at the composition Ni_3Fe, with the crystallographic cubic corner sites occupied by iron atoms and with nickel atoms at the face centres. The superlattice extends over a finite range of composition on either side of Ni_3Fe and for the superlattice the behaviour of both the magnetocrystalline anisotropy and the magnetostriction is a little different. Thus the alloys must be carefully heat-treated to avoid deleterious effects from the unwanted influence of the superlattice. Maximum permeabilities of more than 10^5 and coercivities as low as 2×10^{-7} T (2×10^{-3} Oe) have been achieved in commercial alloys, two of which are called permalloy and supermalloy.

The second group of materials is for such applications as power transformers, generators and motors, with operating frequencies around 50 Hz. Losses of energy due to eddy currents become significant here. The principal requirements of the materials are to give high induction B in moderate fields, coupled with acceptable energy losses. Pure iron is quite a good material in this group, but its properties are much improved by the addition of a few parts per cent (by weight) of silicon in solid solution.

An important effect of the dissolved silicon is to increase the electrical resistivity and so to reduce eddy currents. The other desirable effects are based mainly on metallurgical properties. The saturation magnetization of iron is reduced very little when the silicon is added. Silicon–iron is used in the form of thin polycrystalline sheets. With suitable combinations of rolling and heat treatments grain-oriented sheets containing large crystals (of the order of ten millimetres) can be made commercially. These have a (110) crystallographic plane in the plane of the sheet and a common [001] easy direction of magnetization in the direction of rolling, along the length of the sheet. This optimizes the permeability and reduces the coercivity. In use, the sheets are often built up into closed magnetic circuits with each limb made of easy-direction sheet. Coercivities are higher and maximum permeabilities are lower than for nickel–iron alloys, but maximum inductions are much higher and eddy current losses at power distribution frequencies are smaller.

When soft magnetic materials are required for use at high alternating frequencies new problems arise because of the tendency for eddy currents to be generated, losing energy. For the highest frequencies non-metallic magnetic materials must be used. Such materials are ferrimagnetic rather than ferromagnetic, although the preceding discussion on domain properties in ferromagnets also applies to them. While all ferrites have electrical resistivities at least three orders of magnitude higher than those of conventional metallic ferromagnets, there are wide variations between different ferrites. Some non-metallic magnetic materials have been developed specially for their low electrical conductivity.

The resistivities of ferrites vary between 10^{-2} and 10^{-7} ohm cm and those having relatively low values in this range do produce energy losses due to eddy currents when used in high frequency transformers. Other sources of energy loss at high frequencies are relaxation effects. Spins, either in pure rotation processes or in domain walls, react at a finite rate to oscillatory conditions. Energy is absorbed and the permeability deteriorates. There are also resonance effects that absorb energy.

Those ferrimagnetic oxides that have relatively high permeabilities commonly have coercivities of about 10^{-5} T (10^{-1} Oe). Their energy losses are comparatively high and their use is limited to frequencies below 500 kHz.

High frequency ferrites have relatively low permeabilities at low frequencies but they retain their properties at frequencies up to 10 MHz or more. Some materials of this general kind may be used up to microwave frequencies.

At power frequencies the new amorphous magnetic ribbon materials have a high enough intrinsic resistance to be very attractive for reducing eddy current power losses in power transformers used in electricity distribution. As an example one such transformer rated at 10 kVA consumed only 13 W in its core, compared with 40 W for an equivalent conventional transformer. The potential for savings in the cost of electrical power distribution worldwide is tremendous.

8.5 Hard magnetic materials

The technical requirement of hard magnetic materials is that they shall retain a high state of magnetization when the field that has produced that state is removed. In many applications the magnetization should also be as stable as possible with respect to time and to ambient temperature.

Thus a permanent magnet must have remanence which is as large as possible. The other important requirement is that its coercivity shall be high. A permanent magnet must necessarily possess an internal demagnetizing field the size of which depends on the geometry of the magnet. This is so whether the magnet is straight or whether it forms a nearly closed loop. When no external field is applied the magnetization is set not by the remanence but by that value of the magnetization appropriate to the negative demagnetizing field of value $(B_0)_c$ (Fig. 8.15). The reduction in overall magnetization compared with the remanent value is least when the demagnetizing field is a small proportion of the coercive field; that is, when the coercivity is greatest. Otherwise, when short fat permanent magnets are required that have large demagnetizing fields, only materials of high coercivity are usable.

The effectiveness of a material as a permanet magnet lies in making the magnetization corresponding to the working point as large a proportion as possible of that for zero field. This means that the coercive point must be at as large a negative field as possible and that the hysteresis loop should be as square as possible. Good materials for making permanent magnets have such properties. Modern neodymium–iron–boron alloys have coercivities as high as 6 T (60 kOe).

Devices that use permanent magnets are of two main kinds. In the first of these the permanent magnet properties are used to generate a magnetic field, usually in an air gap between the poles of the magnet. This is used in loudspeakers, galvanometric instruments, dynamos, generators and electric motors. In the second kind the purpose is to generate a force between the magnet and some sort of mobile armature. This is applied in all sorts of lifting and clamping devices.

8.5.1 Energy product as a figure of merit

The performance that can be obtained from a permanent magnet can be broadly defined by a figure of merit, the quantity $(BH)_{max}$. In Figure 8.15 the largest area of the rectangle that can be fitted into the second quadrant of the hysteresis loop is $(BH)_{max}$. This quantity is actually twice the magnetostatic energy per unit volume of the magnet which would be available in an airgap in the magnet having optimum design.

The way the energy product BH varies over the second quadrant of the hysteresis loop is shown in Figure 8.16. The working point produced by the geometry of the magnet usually differs from that which gives the maximum value of the energy product $(BH)_{max}$.

Table 8.3 Energy product parameter of recognized permanent magnet materials

Material	$(BH)_{max}$ $(kJ\,m^{-3})$
Alnico	25
Alcomax	44
Barium ferrite	24
MnBi	44
$SmCo_5$	160
PtCo	74
$Nd_2Fe_{14}B$	360

Table 8.3 gives values of $(BH)_{max}$ for recognized permanent magnet materials. The highest known value is for neodymium–iron–boron alloy, about 360 kJm^{-3} (45 MG Oe).

In highly coercive materials a large amount of magnetostatic energy must be provided in order that the energy barriers that pin down the domain walls may be overcome, nor nucleation of magnetization reversal may be initiated.

A widely-used permanent magnet material is barium ferrite $BaFe_{12}O_{19}$. This has a very large magnetocrystalline anisotropy. The easy direction of magnetization lies along the direction of the six-fold c-axis of the hexagonal crystal structure. Magnets are usually prepared by making use of oriented material. When the ferrite has been prepared having the correct chemical

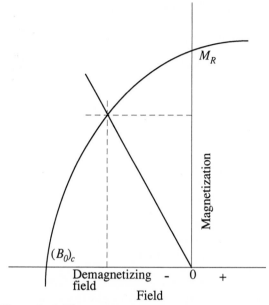

Figure 8.15 The working point of a permanent magnet.

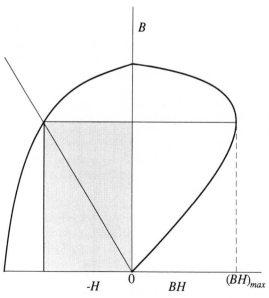

Figure 8.16 Construction used in the design of a permanent magnet showing the definition of $(BH)_{\mathrm{max}}$.

composition it is powdered to a controlled particle size. This must not be too small, or superparamagnetic behaviour will intervene and reduce the available coercivity. The powder is then oriented in a strong magnetic field, compacted and sintered by heating for an extended period at a temperature a little below 1300 °C. In other applications the powder is oriented and dispersed within a matrix of a polymer which is then allowed to harden. The final composite magnet is often flexible.

The physical mechanism of magnetic hardness in barium ferrite is clearly dominated by the high magnetocrystalline anisotropy. In this, as in many other anisotropic uniaxial materials, it is energetically unfavourable for domains of closure to form near the end surfaces of the specimen.

Permanent magnet materials which use shape anisotropy as their basis are the elongated single domain particle materials (ESD). Particles are produced that are small enough to give single domain behaviour and which are sufficiently elongated to have high shape anisotropy and therefore high coercivity. In commercial materials of this kind the particles are usually of iron or iron–cobalt alloy. Again they are dispersed throughout a non-magnetic matrix, aligned in a magnetic field and then compacted into the required external form.

While the single-domain theory outlined in Section 8.3 applies to these materials in principle, it is too simple. Magnetostatic interactions between particles occur and these cause non-coherent modes of magnetization reversal. The coercivity is lower than that expected from the theory.

Alloys of iron, nickel and aluminium form the basis of a very widely used group of permanent magnet materials. There are usually small amounts of other additional elements present. These are heterogeneous alloys in which a ferromagnetic phase is precipitated metallurgically from a solid solution during a carefully controlled heat treatment. The metallurgical state of the alloys is complicated and the conditions for obtaining the best permanent magnet properties are critical. The mechanism for the production of the high coercivity is some combination of shape, strain and magnetocrystalline anisotropy. These act within the magnetic particles precipitated from an alloy matrix.

The greatest growth improvement in figure of merit recently is for magnets containing a rare earth and a transition element. Often the magnets are made either by sintering or plastic-bonding oriented fine particles of alloy. Detailed performance depends on the exact preparation process used. Factors other than magnetic ones often enter into consideration when magnets are being designed.

One remarkable permanent magnetic material is the intermetallic compound $SmCo_5$. The magnetic moment resides mainly on the Co atoms, with the relatively small Sm moment aligned in the opposite sense to the Co moment. The magnetocrystalline anisotropy is very high and sintered specimens have very high coercivities. The exact mechanism of magnetization reversal in $SmCo_5$ is not understood in detail. However, it is thought to be some feature of the domain boundaries being unusually thin (as a result of the high value of the magnetocrystalline anisotropy), these being pinned in an extremely energetic way by macroscopic imperfections in the body of the material.

8.5.2 Neodymium–iron–boron permanent magnets

Very strong permanent magnets based on the alloy $Nd_2Fe_{14}B$ were discovered by Croat et al. (1984) and by Sagawa (1984). Coercivity values at room temperature and energy products are higher than for any other known material. In fact, high coercivities had indeed been observed in binary NdFe alloys as early as 1935, but no permanent magnets were developed then.

The metallurgical state of these alloys is very complicated and is certainly not single-phase. Careful and involved heat treatments are necessary in order to optimize the hard magnetic properties. The phase diagram of the alloys is only known approximately and development of the permanent magnet properties proceeds empirically. There is certainly a main phase present with a composition close to that of the whole alloy. In it both Fe and Nd atoms contribute to the magnetic moment. The presence of several minor phases seems to be necessary for the development of the high coercivity. In production, powders having the final alloy composition are oriented in a magnetic field, pressed and sintered. The final coercivity depends critically on the details of how this process is carried out. The Curie temperature of only 585 K (212 °C) is inconveniently low and the temperature stability of $Nd_2Fe_{14}B$ permanent magnets is relatively poor. Rare earth alloys and compounds are very much subject to corrosion in the atmosphere and it is generally necessary to protect them by means of some surface treatment in order to prolong their life.

The main properties of optimally-treated $Nd_2Fe_{14}B$ are given in Table 8.4.

Table 8.4 Permanent magnet characteristics of optimally-treated $Nd_2Fe_{14}B$

Property	Value
Curie temperature	585 K
	= 212 °C
Anisotropy constant K_1	5 MJm^{-3}
Coercivity	1·2 T
Single domain critical diameter	250 nm
Domain wall thickness	5 nm
$(BH)_{max}$	360 kJm^{-3}
Density (X-ray)	7600 kgm^{-3}

In general the theory of the coercivity of ferromagnetics is not yet quantitatively reliable. Because of the complicated nature of the mathematical problems it has not kept pace with experiment. Recent work has shown that a full consideration of the interplay between domain wall thickness and the effective width and structure of the crystal imperfections and grain boundaries which impede wall motion is the most promising. However, coercivity is controlled by either domain wall pinning or by inhibited nucleation of reverse domains or by a combination of the two. What is really happening tends to be obscured by the intricate metallurgical complications.

8.6 Thin magnetic films and whiskers

There has been much experimental work on domain structures in very thin films of ferromagnetic materials, both single crystal and polycrystalline, and this has added greatly to the knowledge of domain behaviour. Iron whiskers are minute crystals of iron having a high degree of structural perfection which are grown in a special way, such as the reduction of ferrous chloride by hydrogen. These studies have also given much new information on domain characteristics.

8.7 Magnetic bubbles

The particular case that concerns us here is that of a thin single crystal film of a uniaxial ferromagnetic (or ferrimagnetic) material having its easy axis perpendicular to the plane of the film. Such a material might be one of the rare earth garnets, grown with selected orientation by an epitaxial method from the vapour phase. A typical film thickness is about $20\,\mu m$ $(2 \times 10^{-3}\,cm)$. In such a specimen the domain structure may be observed in transmitted light using the Faraday effect.

When the specimen is initially demagnetized it contains equal areas magnetized up and down. Applying a relatively small field perpendicular to the film causes the unfavoured domains to shrink (Fig. 8.17). When there is no marked anisotropy within the plane of the film the domain walls wander irregularly over the surface of the film guided by minor stresses and imperfections (Fig. 8.18a). Applying a fixed field that is insufficient for saturation is observed to make the unfavoured domains thinner (Fig. 8.18b). When a larger pulsed field of the same sign is superimposed on the steady field the negative domains start to break up into small cylindrical domains called bubbles which are then stable (Fig. 8.18c). Repeating the pulse produces more bubbles (Fig. 8.18d). The bubble domains are magnetic dipoles that mutually repel each other and that can be moved about the specimen by applying field gradients. Their diameter is of the order of a few micrometres.

Bubble domains have a large potential in device applications, particularly in computers. They can be guided through specimens on tracks and made to take part in logic operations. A moving line of bubbles is equivalent to a moving recorder tape coated with magnetic oxide, but is much more versatile. Their applications are illustrated in Chapter 9.

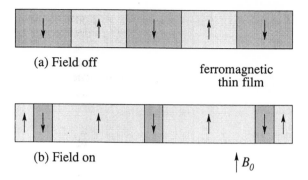

(a) Field off

ferromagnetic
thin film

(b) Field on B_0

Figure 8.17 Transverse domains in a uniaxial thin film.

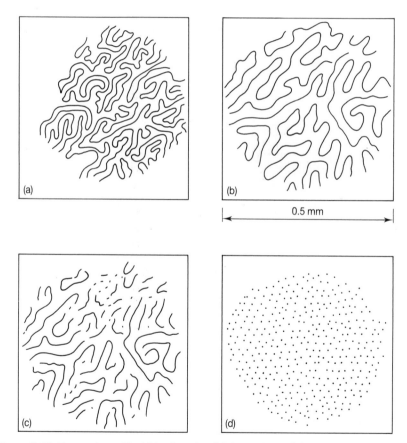

0.5 mm

Figure 8.18 Formation of bubble domains (a) in no field, (b) in a fixed small field, (c) after one superimposed pulse and (d) after several pulses (from Crangle, 1977, *The Magnetic Properties of Solids*, Fig. 6.16, Edward Arnold, after O'Dell, 1974, *Magnetic Bubbles*, Macmillan).

Chapter 9 ⎯⎯⎯⎯⎯⎯⎯⎯⎯⎯⎯

Applications of magnetism

Applications of magnetism are of two main kinds. There are applications of magnetic properties and magnetic measuring techniques to problems in wider areas, such as in metallurgy or in chemistry. There are also the uses of the magnetic properties of materials to provide devices of wide applicability.

9.1 Permanent magnets

Examples of device applications of permanent magnets are electric motors of low power or small size, electric generators, moving coil meters, loudspeakers, magnetic separators, control devices for electron beams, and magnetic holding applications.

Each application creates its own problems of design and quite often differing materials are used for different kinds of application. Sometimes the aim is to maximize the scientific performance. But many applications are for mass production and a commercial compromise is necessary to balance the conflict between the best scientific properties and the cost.

9.1.1 Energy associated with a magnetic field

Consider a toroidal coil (Fig. 9.1) having N turns, mean circumference l and area of cross section A, and let an increasing current be supplied. A back emf will be induced in the coil proportional to the rate of change of flux Φ enclosed.

While the current is changing, work is being done at the rate

$$dW/dt = i(N\, d\Phi/dt) = i(NA\, dB/dt) \tag{9.1}$$

where B is the induction within the coil. Since the magnetic excitation H produced by the current is

$$H = iN/l \tag{9.2}$$

Equation (9.1) becomes

$$dW/dt = (iN/l)Al\, dB/dt = HV\, dB/dt \tag{9.3}$$

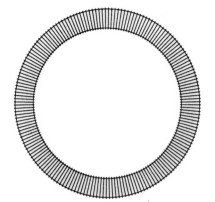

Figure 9.1 Toroidal coil.

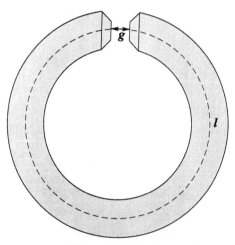

Figure 9.2 Ring-shaped permanent magnet.

where $V = Al$ is the volume enclosed by the coil. Thus the energy involved in setting up a field B_0 is

$$W = V/\mu_0 \int B_0 \, dB \tag{9.4}$$

In free space $\mu_r = 1$ and $B = B_0$ so that

$$W = VB_0^2/2\mu_0 = 1/2VB_0H \tag{9.5}$$

The energy per unit volume in a field in free space is

$$E = 1/2B_0^2/\mu_0 = 1/2B_0H \, \text{Jm}^{-3} \text{ (in SI, or erg cm}^{-3} \text{ in cgs)} \tag{9.6}$$

9.1.2 Energy of a permanent magnet

Let us consider now the ring-shaped permanent magnet shown in Figure 9.2. If there are no electric currents we may write, for the whole magnetic circuit (see Equation (4.29))

$$\oint H.dl = 0 \tag{9.7}$$

In a perfect system free from magnetic leakage and where the field is everywhere uniform

$$H_g g + H_m l = 0 \tag{9.8}$$

where $H_g(=(B_0)g/\mu_0)$ and $H_m(=(B_0)m/\mu_0)$ are respectively the magnetic excitations in the gap and in the magnet. Across the gap the flux must be continuous.

$$B_g A_g = B_m A_m \tag{9.9}$$

where A_g and A_m are the areas of cross section of gap and magnet respectively.

$$\text{Thus} \quad H_g g B_g A_g = -H_m l B_m A_m = 1/2 B_m H_m V_m \tag{9.10}$$

where V_g and V_m are respectively the volumes of gap and magnet.

The left hand side of Equation (9.10) is the magnetic energy stored in the gap of the magnet (see Equation (9.6)). Apart from the geometrical relationship between V_g and V_m this is given by the product

$$B_m H_m = 1/\mu_0 B_m (B_0)_m \tag{9.11}$$

This product is called the energy product of the magnet. It varies between different parts of the hysteresis loop of the permanent magnet material (Fig. 8.16). Its maximum value is usually used as a figure of merit characteristic of the material (Table 8.3). In comparing the permanent magnet properties of materials it is usual to use induction hysteresis loops (Fig. 1.1).

The working condition of a permanent magnet is set by its demagnetizing field (Fig. 8.15) and this depends mostly on the geometry of the magnet. Writing $\mu_0 H_g = (B_0)_g$ in Equation (9.10) and $B_g = (B_0)_g$ for the air gap in which the relative permeability μ_r is effectively unity

$$1/\mu_0 (B_0)_g^2 = -(B_m H_m) V_m / V_g \tag{9.12}$$

To obtain the highest field in the gap the energy product of the magnet must therefore have its maximum value. If the volume of the air gap is predetermined the designer of the magnet must select a material and a magnet shape so that the magnet works near $(BH)_{max}$. This is not always straightforward, due to several complicating factors which we have ignored here.

In many applications the stability of the field produced by a permanent magnet is important. Since the spontaneous magnetization varies with temperature, so must the induction and thus the field produced in the air gap. One consequence is that the sensitivity of moving coil meters is not altogether independent of the ambient temperature. Another is that the torque of motors incorporating permanent magnets falls as the working temperature rises. It is therefore desirable that permanent magnet materials should have Curie temperatures as high as possible.

9.2 Applications of soft magnetic materials

Soft magnetic materials are used widely as cores for transformers and inductors. The properties required in a soft magnetic material are a small coercivity, a large saturation magnetization, large initial and maximum permeability and a small hysteresis loss. To some extent these requirements conflict and the selection of material for a given application is a compromise. Table 9.1 summarizes some of the properties available.

Table 9.1 Properties of some soft magnetic materials

Material	Induction coercivity (T)	Maximum permeability (T)	Remanent induction (T)
Pure iron	10^{-6}	350 000	2·2
Silicon iron	$1·5 \times 10^{-5}$	40 000	2·0
Supermalloy	4×10^{-7}	10^6	0·8
MnZn ferrite	3×10^{-5}	5000	0·3

Almost all devices used in the generation, distribution and large scale use of electrical power depend on the use of FeSi alloys. Power supplies are nearly always alternating and the supply frequency is almost universally either 50 Hz or 60 Hz. The material of the magnetic circuits in transformers, generators and motors therefore carries an alternating flux and this produces eddy currents when the material is metallic. These are a source of energy loss. Non-metallic magnetic materials are not generally suitable for these applications because their saturation induction (flux density) is too low. The new amorphous ferromagnetic materials have high electrical resistance and they have a good potential here.

Because of eddy currents the magnetic flux tends to concentrate near the surface of the magnetic material, leading to poor magnetic utilization of the material as well as the energy loss due to the eddy currents themselves. These effects get worse at higher frequencies. Magnetic circuits working at about 50 Hz and employing silicon–iron are usually built of laminations typically about 0·33 mm (0·013 inch) thick having a thin surface coating of insulation. Skin effects are thereby lessened and the induction is nearly uniform across the thickness of the laminations.

The addition of silicon to iron is beneficial for several reasons. The most important is that it increases the electrical resistivity considerably. Also, the magnetocrystalline anisotropy is reduced, leading to easier movement of domain boundary walls and lower coercivity. Another reason is that more than about 2 per cent of silicon (see Fig. 9.12) suppresses the formation of the fcc γ-phase at high temperatures. Annealing processes aimed at promoting grain growth during the preparation of grain-oriented material can take place wholly within the bcc α-phase and this is beneficial. There is no destructive γ- to α-phase transformation on cooling.

Commercial silicon–iron sheet often has a grain size of several millimetres and in the best material more than 90 per cent of the grains are oriented within a few degrees of having a (110) plane in the plane of the sheet and a [001] easy direction along the length of the sheet. Such material has an induction of about 1·8 T (18 000 G) in a field of 10^{-3} T (10 Oe). The total rate of energy loss of such material when in use in the form of standard laminations is typically about 1 W kg^{-1}. Amorphous ferromagnetic metals have considerably smaller losses.

One application of the group of materials based on nickel–iron alloys is in magnetic screening, useful for protecting various electronic components (for example television tubes) from the effects of stray magnetic fields. Here the property required is that the induction shall be as large as possible in a very small field, in order that as much flux as possible shall be carried within the body of the screening material. That is, a relative permeability μ_r is required that is as large as possible in small fields. Some alloys reach an induction B of about 0·6 T (6000 G) in a field of 2×10^{-6} T (2×10^{-2} Oe). That the saturation induction is little greater than this value is relatively unimportant since it is often possible to increase the flux that can be carried by the screen by making it thicker.

When inductors or transformers having cores of magnetic materials are required to work at high frequencies, only non-metallic magnetic materials may be used, generally soft ferrites. Different materials are chosen for different kinds of application.

Ferrite-cored inductors are used as elements in frequency-selective circuits in a wide variety of electronic equipment. In carrier telephony especially, the performance and stability of such components is critical, in order that the resonant frequency of a circuit shall not wander with changes in ambient conditions. The form of a ferrite pot core inductor is shown in Figure 9.3. The windings of the coil occupy the central spaces. This form is

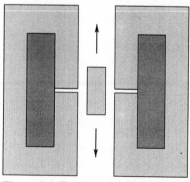

Figure 9.3 Ferrite pot core inductor.

chosen so as to minimize magnetic coupling between adjacent components in an electrical circuit. The purpose of the magnetic shunt placed centrally is to allow the inductor to be adjusted to a required value of inductance. High quality cored inductors are usually operated at very low amplitudes of field, so as to avoid hysteresis and other non-linear effects.

Another application of soft ferrites is in making ferrite antennas for radio receivers. Almost all broadcast receivers using amplitude modulation that are now manufactured are provided with internal ferrite rod antennas. A short circular coil of N turns enclosing an area A is placed with its axis parallel to the magnetic field vector of the alternating signal being received. The aperture of the winding is filled with a relatively long ferrite cylinder of relative permeability μ_r. It is coaxial with the coil and its centre coincides with the centre of the coil. The emf E induced in the coil is given by

$$E = E_0 \mu_r 2\pi A N / \lambda \qquad (9.13)$$

where λ is the wavelength (in metres) and E_0 is the electric field strength of the signal being received. For a material selected to work at 1 MHz, μ_r is typically about 1000. For another chosen to work at 30 MHz, μ_r is more commonly 100.

9.3 Magnetic tape recording

Magnetic tapes are used for the long term storage of information. The magnetic material with which the tape is coated remembers its previous state of magnetization and the stored information may be retrieved subsequently by a reading process. There are two basically different kinds of operation. In computing, the level of the stored signal is relatively unimportant since it is only necessary to distinguish between binary code signals 0 or 1. However, writing and reading takes place at high speed. Data transfer rates are 10^4 bits per second or more. When speech is being recorded the signal level is important and only a little distortion is acceptable. For the recording of music it is the absence of distortion that matters most. In audio applications the speeds of writing and reading are relatively slow.

A magnetic tape consists of a tape made of plastic material on to which is stuck a magnetic powder embedded in a plastic matrix. Commercial tapes use magnetic gamma ferric oxide (γ-Fe_2O_3) and chromium dioxide (CrO_2). The particles of the powder are needle-shaped.

The magnetic properties of γ-Fe_2O_3 are important. We start with another iron oxide, magnetite Fe_3O_4. This is a ferrimagnetic inverse spinel of the type described in Section 6.2.5. When Fe_3O_4 is heated in an oxidizing atmosphere, γ-Fe_2O_3 is formed. This is unstable and transforms on heating to temperatures above 400 °C to α-Fe_2O_3, which is antiferromagnetic and unwanted in the present context.

γ-Fe_2O_3 is ferrimagnetic and its structure can be considered as a defect inverse spinel. The oxidation of Fe_3O_4 may be seen as an introduction of

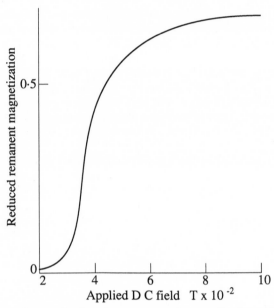

Figure 9.4 Dependence of minor-loop remanent magnetization of gamma-Fe_2O_3 on the maximum static field previously applied (after Mee, 1964, *Physics of Magnetic Recording*, North Holland).

vacancies preferentially in an ordered way on to some of the spinel B-sites in place of some of the iron, thereby increasing the O/Fe ratio. The magnetic moment of γ-Fe_2O_3 is 2·5 μ_B per Fe_2O_3 molecule, compared with 4 μ_B per molecule for Fe_3O_4. The Curie temperature of γ-Fe_2O_3 is about 90 K higher than that of Fe_3O_4.

The shape of the particles of magnetite from which γ-Fe_2O_3 is produced controls the shape of the final particles, and depends on which of two methods are used to prepare the magnetite. The two shapes have distinctly different magnetic properties. Most tapes contain single-domain acicular particles oriented in the direction of motion of the tape. They are typically about 0·5 μm long with a length/width ratio of between 5 and 10. Shape anisotropy controls their magnetization characteristics. The coercivity of tape material is about $2·5 \times 10^{-2}$ T (250 Oe).

What is of interest for recording purposes is how the minor-loop remanent magnetization varies with the maximum field previously applied. Such a relationship is shown in Figure 9.4, for static applied fields.

Let us now consider how information may be written on a tape. The tape is driven at constant velocity, about 5 cm sec^{-1}, with its plastic base in contact with a series of transducers. Each transducer (Fig. 9.5) consists of a magnetic ring of high permeability having a coil wound round it. The coil is used either to magnetize the ring when writing or to detect changes in the flux in the ring when reading. The leakage field at the gap in the ring writes on the tape. So that the greatest possible amount of information may be stored on the tape the gap is as narrow as possible. The first transducer erases any previous signal on the tape by applying a high frequency .alternating signal, the second writes and the third reads.

If the signal being recorded were simply applied to the writing trans-ducer the remanent magnetization written on the tape would be far from a linear function of the applied field, as Figure 9.4 shows. It is usually necessary to introduce some method of restoring linearity. The most common method is to mix the signal field with a bias field consisting of an alternating signal of high frequency and of an optimum amplitude. The bias field does not remain written on the tape. The remanent signal that does appear on the tape can be made proportional to the magnetizing signal to a fairly high degree, so long as the signal amplitude is not so great as to approach saturation.

Differing tape speeds are used for different signal frequencies. Video recording of frequencies up to 3 MHz uses tape speeds about one hundred times greater than those normally used for audio recording. For audio and video purposes magnetic tape technology is now being replaced by optical methods that are beyond the scope of this account. In data storage the magnetic media are being retained because of the continual need to overwrite.

9.4 Applications of magnetic bubbles

The chief potential application of magnetic bubbles is in providing compact and versatile data storage for computing. At the time of writing no bubble data stores are yet in regular commercial use. They have specialized applications.

In Section 8.7 we saw how bubble domains may be produced in thin uniaxial magnetic films having their easy direction of magnetization normal to the plane of the film. The aim here is to indicate how bubbles may be used in technical devices.

The physical characteristics required of the material in which bubbles are to be produced are quite critical. For stable bubbles to form, their magnetization must be accurately perpendicular to the plane of the film. This occurs when the uniaxial magnetocrystalline anisotropy energy K_u is significantly greater than the magnetostatic energy given by $1/2\,\mu_0 M_s^2$, where M_s is the saturation magnetization. A quality factor Q is often used for bubble materials which expresses the ratio of these two energies

$$Q = 2\,\mu_0 K_u / (\mu_0 M)^2 \tag{9.14}$$

The value of Q is typically five. Also for stability, the bubble length (equal to the film thickness) must not be significantly greater than the bubble diameter and this is usually a few μm. The domain wall thickness is about 0·1 μm.

Another important parameter is called the characteristic length λ. Bubble formation depends on the ratio λ/h, where h is the film thickness. Bubble diameters are usually about 10λ. λ depends on the intrinsic

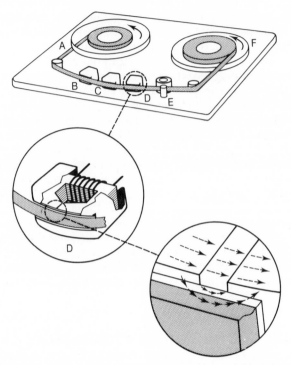

Figure 9.5 Writing on and reading from magnetic tapes (after Mee, loc cit from Crangle, 1977, *The Magnetic Properties of Solids*, Fig. 8.11, Edward Arnold).

properties of the bubble material, in particular being proportional to $Q^{1/2}/M_s$. Calculated and measured values of λ agree only approximately: usual values are about 0.1 μm.

Materials that satisfy all these criteria are garnets, such as substituted YIG of the type $(EuY)_3(GaFe)_5O_{12}$ (see Section 6.2.7). Suitably oriented single crystal films are grown epitaxially. There is a variety of techniques and liquid phase epitaxy is commonly used. A nonmagnetic substrate having the correct structure and lattice parameter is selected and oriented: gadolinium gallium garnet $Gd_3Ga_5O_{12}$ is used. The substrate is dipped for a controlled time into a flux solution of the correct composition held near saturation conditions at high temperature. An epitaxial film of the solute crystal grows on the surface of the substrate, from which it can subsequently be removed.

Having considered the medium in which bubbles may be formed we must now consider how they may be controlled usefully in the medium. The first requirement is a track along which bubbles may be moved and stored. Several types of track are possible but we consider only one.

It was shown in Section 8.7 that a bias field must always be applied normal to the film in order that bubbles can exist. A pattern of T and I bars made of soft magnetic material is deposited on the surface of the garnet by evaporation, as in Figure 9.6. The soft material is usually an alloy similar to permalloy. The width of the bars is about half the bubble diameter and their length is about five times their width, about 15 μm. The bar thickness is not very important, but is often about 0·1 μm.

When the overlay is magnetized by superimposing a driving field in the plane of the film, the stray fields round the bars provide potential wells in which bubbles may be held. Rotating the driving field within the plane of the surface changes the position of the potential wells and this enables the controlled movement of bubbles. Referring to Figure 9.6, let the polarities be such that when the drive field is in direction 1 the bubble is attracted to location 1, the upright of the T being magnetized along its length. Rotating the field clockwise through directions 1 to 8 provides a sequence of stable locations 1 to 8, driving the bubble towards the right, from the centre of one T to the centre of the next. Since the repeat distance of the overlay pattern is about 25 μm, there are about 400 bubble locations per centimetre of track. When the track spacing is about 40 μm there are roughly 10^4 locations per cm^2 of garnet surface. Rotation of the driving field is achieved by the use of static coils having their axes perpendicular to each other and parallel to the film, with appropriate phase control of the currents in each.

The maximum possible driving frequencies depend on the detailed form of the overlay pattern used, being as high as 500 kHz in some cases. Bubble velocities are a few m s^{-1}. A location which holds a bubble counts as one in the computer binary register and an empty location counts as zero.

Bubble generation by the use of pulsed fields as outlined in Section 8.7 is difficult to operate and control when overlays are in use. A large and continuously replenished source domain is held by a relatively large permalloy disc, as shown in Figure 9.7. As the driving field rotates, bubble domains break off and they are injected into the track. When a zero is required to be injected a suitable conductor placed near the point of

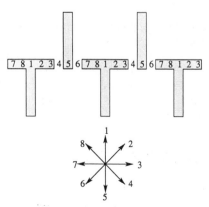

Figure 9.6 Magnetic overlay track made of soft magnetic T and I bars, illustrating how magnetic bubbles transmit (after O'Dell, loc cit).

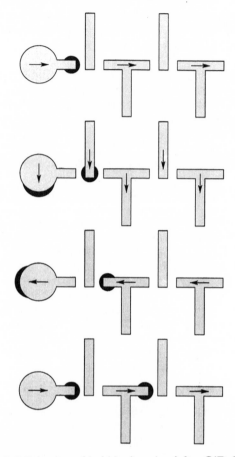

Figure 9.7 Injection of bubble domains (after O'Dell, loc cit).

injection is energized. This prevents a bubble from being launched for chosen rotations of the drive field (Fig. 9.8).

Bubbles are detected with a suitably placed magneto-resistive sensor that indicates the presence of a bubble from the stray field that it generates, and the output from the sensor is taken away as an electrical signal.

One of the most important advantages of this procedure is that there are no mechanical parts that might be subject to friction and wear.

9.5 Imaging by nuclear magnetic resonance (NMR)

It is possible to use nuclear magnetic resonance to form two-dimensional and three-dimensional spin density images in solids and liquids. An

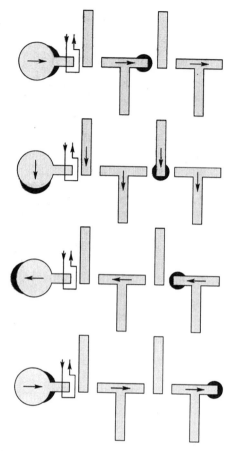

Figure 9.8 Injection of zero signal into bubble track (after O'Dell, loc cit).

important application is the ability to form images of biological tissue in the living state. The method is non-invasive and the tissue is not harmed.

The method mostly uses NMR with protons. This is particularly advantageous, first because ^{1}H is a sensitive nucleus and second because protons as the hydrogen atoms in water are very plentiful in biological materials. In human medicine, NMR imaging has its major impact in the study of mobile protons distributed within the human body. The human body normally contains approximately two thirds of its weight as water and this is distributed quite differently among the various types of tissue and organs. Contrast between different areas is produced by differing proton concentrations. Other important NMR parameters that are used to characterize spins in a particular environment are the spin–lattice and the spin–spin relaxation times and the self-diffusion coefficient, among others.

In ordinary NMR, measurements are made in as uniform a magnetic field as possible. Then all the magnetically active spins within the sample resonate at approximately the same Larmor resonance angular frequency ω, given by $\omega = \gamma B_0$, where B_0 is the magnitude of the magnetic field acting on the sample and γ is the gyromagnetic ratio for protons. Small variations in the resonant frequency are the result of different influences on the protons arising from their detailed environment. The profile of signal strength against frequency is an expression of the relative numbers of proton spins subject to these influences. Normally non-uniformity in the applied field strength from the magnet imposes broadening on the resonance signal which masks the fundamental effects and this is unwanted.

If a field gradient that varies linearly with position is superimposed on the steady uniform field the shape of the resonance signal becomes an indicator of the number of proton spins as a function of position. We have spatial differentiation and it is possible to calibrate the gradient so that positional coordinates can be applied to the resonance signal. A projection is produced on the spin density in a direction orthogonal to the gradient. Altering the relative angle between sample and gradient leads to the ability to build up two-dimensional and three-dimensional pictures.

In modern applications a more adaptable method is used. It is important to be able to define an active volume of spins lying within an extended object which yields NMR signals that are distinct from those from surrounding material and that are unperturbed by them. This is achieved by using shaped RF pulses in combination with rapidly switched magnetic field gradients.

With NMR imaging techniques it is also possible to differentiate between regions of the specimen that have different spin–lattice relaxation times characteristic of the local microscopic motion of the molecules which contain the protons, even where the proton density is constant. The results obtained are important in medical diagnosis. The sensitivity of this measurement may be improved by injecting minor, safe quantities of other elements that concentrate in the regions under examination and strongly affect the relaxation times.

The presentation of the image depends on applying sophisticated computing techniques in order to process the raw signals. The final image appears on a computer screen. The methods have become increasingly powerful.

In very recent years as larger and faster computers have been developed the time required to produce an image comprises the data acquisition time and the computational time. With the best computers the data acquisition time usually dominates. Rapid imaging is particularly important when the object is moving, to avoid blurring or to allow real-time observations to be made. An example of the latter might be to observe the working of a human heart.

The magnetic fields are generated by superconducting magnets so large that there is an uncooled region along their axis where a human patient can rest. One of the major obstacles to the implementation of ultra-high speed imaging techniques is the generation of large, rapidly switched gradients and in avoiding the unwanted side effects that they produce.

These methods of specimen imaging are already very important and as the technology improves they are expected to have even wider application.

9.6 Magnetic phase analysis of alloys

In constitutional studies of alloys that contain more than one phase it is often important to be able to measure the proportion of each phase present, or to determine the compositions of the phases. In favourable circumstances magnetic measurements may be used to obtain such information, often complementing the use of other techniques. These magnetic methods are very powerful for attacking constitutional problems in metals and alloys but they have not really been used as much as their potential would merit.

9.6.1 Ferromagnetic materials

The intrinsic magnetization $\sigma_{B,T}$ of a ferromagnet is a unique function of field and temperature which is insensitive to experimental conditions and to the degree of mixing with other materials. So long as the field is strong enough to eliminate domain effects, variations of field have a small effect on the intrinsic magnetization and it differs little from the spontaneous magnetization $\sigma_{0,T}$, except near T_C (Fig. 1.3). The relationship between $\sigma_{0,T}$ and the temperature T characterizes a material, or a composition within a solid solution. The dependence of T_C on composition may be determined for a given phase from preliminary measurements under single-phase conditions. When the same phase is present in a multiphase alloy its composition may be found by measuring its Curie temperature.

This procedure may be followed whether the other phases present are ferromagnetic or not, but there must be no possibility of confusion between their respective Curie temperatures.

In a multiphase alloy the observed dependence of spontaneous magnetization on temperature is the sum of the independent effects from all the separate phases, combined according to their proportions. It is sufficient to take the magnetization (per unit mass) measured in a single strong field to represent the spontaneous magnetization.

Let the measured (spontaneous) magnetization of the alloy at temperatures T_1, T_2, T_3, ... be σ_1, σ_2, σ_3, ... Let us suppose that the phases present have been identified qualitatively and that their magnetic characteristics are capable of being established in a separate experiment. At these same temperatures the respective magnetizations of one of the phases are a_1, a_2, a_3, ..., and so on for the other phases, giving b_1, b_2, b_3, ... c_1, c_2, c_3. Let the respective fractions of these phases be $x, y, z, \ldots$ Then

$$a_1 x + b_1 y + c_1 z + \ldots = \sigma_1$$
$$a_2 x + b_2 y + c_2 z + \ldots = \sigma_2$$
$$a_3 x + b_3 y + c_3 z + \ldots = \sigma_3$$
$$a_n x + b_n y + c_n z + \ldots = \sigma_n \tag{9.15}$$

Simultaneous solution of Equation (9.15) now gives the proportions of the phases. The coefficient for one of the phases may have the value zero at all temperatures (that is, one phase can be non-magnetic), but if two or more of the phases have an identical dependence of magnetization on temperature, their proportions will appear lumped together in the final result. Otherwise the result is unique.

The sensitivity of the analysis is greatest when the temperatures are chosen so as to emphasize the differences between the phases. Analysis by this method is simplest when the ferromagnetic phases involved are of fixed composition, although this is not essential. However, the dependence of spontaneous magnetization on temperature for the phases and compositions actually present is known accurately.

Figure 9.9 illustrates the application of magnetic phase analysis to an

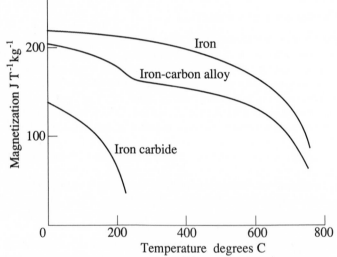

Figure 9.9 Magnetic phase analysis of an iron–carbon alloy.

iron–carbon alloy (a carbon steel) containing 1·73 per cent of carbon by weight, and free from significant impurities. In its annealed state it consists of body-centred cubic iron having a very small amount of carbon in solid solution (called ferrite) and a precipitated iron carbide Fe_3C (called cementite). Both phases are ferromagnetic and the (σ/T) graph of the alloy is as shown in Figure 9.9. The (σ/T) graphs of Fe and Fe_3C are also shown. Calculation gives 0·262 for the fraction of Fe_3C and 0·769 for the fraction of Fe. The difference between the sum of these two fractions and unity is a measure of the error inherent in the analysis. Since Fe_3C contains 6·69 per cent of carbon by weight, the indicated composition is $6·69 \times 0·262 = 1·75$ per cent by weight, agreeing well with the chemical analysis.

9.6.2 Paramagnetic materials

A similar analysis is possible in the paramagnetic state, but only for no more than two phases, these having known and widely differing susceptibilities. One application is the measurement of the amounts of the bcc and fcc phases in iron-rich binary alloys at high temperatures.

In pure iron at temperatures above the Curie temperature the α-phase (body-centred cubic) and the γ-phase (face-centred cubic) are both paramagnetic and their susceptibilities differ widely. This difference remains in binary iron-rich alloys. It provides a method for determining the boundaries of the γ-loop regions in equilibrium diagrams.

The susceptibility of each phase acts independently and at a given temperature the mass susceptibility χ of a mixture of the γ- and α-phases is given by

$$\chi = y\chi_\gamma + (1-y)\chi_\alpha \tag{9.16}$$

where y is the proportion by weight of γ-phase present, and χ_γ and χ_α refer to the γ- and the α-phases respectively at the temperature chosen. χ_γ and χ_α are not independent of temperature. They vary smoothly in a way that allows extrapolation from single-phase conditions to temperatures where mixed phases exist, allowing the proportions of the phases present to be estimated.

The boundaries of the γ-loop in the equilibrium diagram of the Fe–Si alloy system have been determined using this method, as follows.

In alloys the α- to γ-phase change shows marked temperature hysteresis, because diffusion is involved and the change is not instantaneous. This hysteresis may be seen in Figure 9.10. How the proportion of γ-phase depends on temperature depends on the direction of the temperature change and on the rate of change of temperature. Equilibrium conditions lie somewhere between those for heating and cooling. The following procedure allows the equilibrium conditions to be recognized.

If a specimen is heated from a lower temperature into the region of the phase transformation and then the heating process is halted, the specimen will be in a non-equilibrium two-phase state possessing less γ-phase than the equilibrium amount. If it is then cooled slowly at a constant rate the amount of γ-phase will continue to increase at a diminishing rate until equilibrium is reached, after which it will decrease. The maximum represents a point on the graph of the equilibrium proportions of phases against temperature. The procedure may be repeated for a series of different initial states and the equilibrium graph for the alloy is the locus of the maxima. The converse procedure may be applied involving initial cooling and slow reheating of the specimen. The method is illustrated in Figure 9.11. Repeating with a series of alloy compositions traces out the phase diagram (Fig. 9.12).

This general method is a useful tool in suitable circumstances. It has been used to study martensitic transformations in steels. These are time-dependent changes between the bcc and the fcc states which occur after rapid quenching from high temperature and subsequent re-heating.

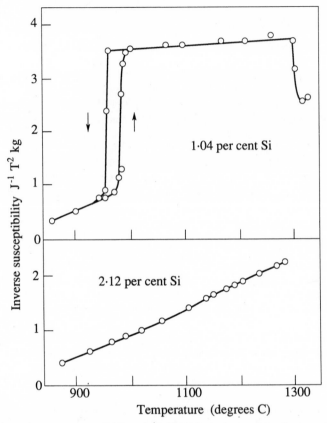

Figure 9.10 Inverse susceptibility plotted against temperature for two iron–silicon alloys.

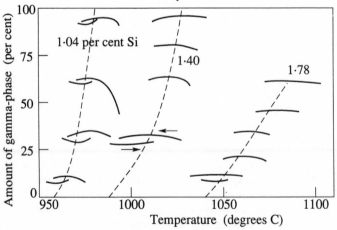

Figure 9.11 Method of recognizing phase equilibrium in analysis of iron–silicon alloys.

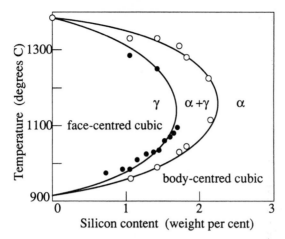

Figure 9.12 Gamma-loop in the iron–silicon phase diagram, determined by magnetic phase analysis.

Bibliography

Anderson, JC (1968). *Magnetism and magnetic materials*. Chapman and Hall.

Bacon, GE (1962). *Neutron diffraction 2nd edition*. Oxford.

Barbara, B; Gignoux, D and Vettier, C (1988). *Lectures on modern magnetism*. Springer.

Bates, LF (1963). *Modern magnetism 4th edition*. Cambridge.

Belov, KP (1959). *Magnetic transitions*. Consultants Bureau.

Berkowitz, AE and Kneller, E (1969). *Magnetism and metallurgy vols 1 and 2*. Academic Press.

Birss, RR (1966). *Symmetry and Magnetism*. North Holland.

Bozorth, RM (1951). *Ferromagnetism*. Van Nostrand.

Brailsford, F (1966). *Physical principles of magnetism*. Van Nostrand.

Carey, R and Isaac, ED (1966). *Magnetic domains and techniques for their observation*. EUP.

Carlin, RL (1986). *Magnetochemistry*. Springer.

Chakravarty, AS (1980). *Introduction to the magnetic properties of solids*. Wiley.

Chen, CW (1977). *Magnetism and metallurgy of soft magnetic materials*. North Holland.

Chikazumi, S (1964). *Physics of magnetism*. Wiley.

Chowdhury, D (1986). *Spin glasses and other frustrated systems*. World Scientific.

Cracknell, AP (1975). *Magnetism in crystalline materials*. Pergamon.

Craik, DJ (1975). *Magnetic oxides*. Wiley.

Cullity, BD (1972). *Introduction to magnetic materials*. Addison–Wesley.

Ferchmin, AR and Kobe, S (1983). *Amorphous magnetism and metallic magnetic materials*. North Holland.

Goodenough, JB (1966). *Magnetism and the chemical bond*. Wiley.

Heck, C (1974). *Magnetic materials and their applications*. Butterworth.

Jiles, D (1991). *Introduction to magnetism and magnetic materials*. Chapman and Hall.

Kalvius, GM and Tebble, RS (1979). *Experimental magnetism*. Wiley.

Kittel, C (1986). *Introduction to solid state physics 6th edition*. Wiley.

Martin, DH (1967). *Magnetism in solids*. Iliffe.

Mattis, DC (1965). *The theory of magnetism*. Harper and Row.

Morrish, AH (1980). *The physical principles of magnetism*. Krieger, New York.

Myers, HP (1990). *Introductory solid state physics*. Taylor and Francis.

O'Dell, TH (1974). *Magnetic bubbles*. Macmillan.

Rado, GT and Suhl, H (1963–1973). *Magnetism vols 1–5*. Academic Press.

Smart, JS (1966). *Effective field theories of magnetism*. Saunders.

Standley, KJ (1972). *Oxide magnetic materials*. Oxford.

Stoner, EC (1934). *Magnetism and matter*. Methuen.
Tebble, RS and Craik, DJ (1969). *Magnetic materials*. Wiley.
Van Vleck, JH (1932). *The theory of electric and magnetic susceptibilities*. Oxford.
White, RM (1970). *Quantum theory of magnetism*. McGraw Hill.
Williams, DEG (1966). *The magnetic properties of matter*. Longmans.
Wohlfarth, EP (ed.) (1980–90). *Ferromagnetic materials vols 1–5*. North Holland.
   (Buschow, KHJ and Wohlfarth, EP: ed. for vol. 5.)
Zeiger, HJ and Pratt, GW (1973). *Magnetic interactions in solids*. Oxford.
Zijlstra, H (1967). *Experimental Methods in Magnetism*, 2 vols. North Holland.

Index